return
to slender
after weight-loss surgery

First published in 2010 by Bariatric Cookery (UK) Ltd,
Stamford Place, Crawley Drive, Camberley, Surrey, GU15 2AB
www.bariatriccookery.com

Cataloguing in Publication Data: a catalogue record for this
book is available from the British Library.

ISBN: 978-0-9566626-0-6

Designed by Andrea Rumsey, Rumseyshort
Kings Court, 91-93 High Street, Camberley, Surrey, GU15 3RN
www.rumseyshort.co.uk

Printed by Aaron Printing Ltd

Contents

Return to slender

Back in October 2009 I found myself travelling to Chichester to meet Shaw Somers. I had an appointment to meet the renowned 'Fat Doctor'. I was going to ask him about bariatric (weight-loss) surgery because I felt I had reached the end of the road when it came to self-administered diets. All the way there I kept asking myself 'How and why have things come to this?' For the uncomfortable fact is that I am a prolific food writer, have a good knowledge of nutrition, have steely self-control in so many areas of my life, success on so many fronts but could not solve my weight issues and boy had I tried.

Name a diet and I had tried it – those associated with slimming clubs, special meal replacement regimes, the latest diet book sensation and many more that I would rather not admit to since they involved injections, pills and hypnosis. On the seat next to me was what I called my 'Fatty File' – called and labelled such (for all to see) because I was very much aware (and to be honest ashamed) that I was fat. I was not just stocky, chubby, porky, on-the-large-side, comfortable, big-boned or any other term that disguised the unpalatable truth, but FAT. This file was stuffed fit to burst with information on the latest diets, treatments, testimonials and finally, surgical procedures available today. Having done all of this research work I had come to the conclusion that if anyone could help me then Shaw Somers could. This was to be my last ditch attempt to sort things out.

Not surprisingly, as a food writer, I have always eaten well. My problem wasn't a bad diet based on fast food that can be nutritionally poor. In fact I have always eaten good, wholesome food that scores well on paper and plate. No, my problem was the quantity of it that I ate. Food was my friend (and enemy), my way to express love and caring, my work and the way I earn a living, and the vehicle through which I express my creative side. From a very early age I have cooked for myself and for others, made money through it, expressed myself with it and enjoyed life alongside or around it. However, that relationship had soured and was literally eating away at me! I realised that if I continued to eat the amount I did and gain weight year-on-year then my future looked bleak. The 'happy-go-lucky, bouncy food writer' (as I was often described) was in real danger of becoming more and more immobile, breathless, depressed and well, cheesed-off. I was tired of playing the happy fat friend, the food-loving gourmet and the big writer with a waistline to match.

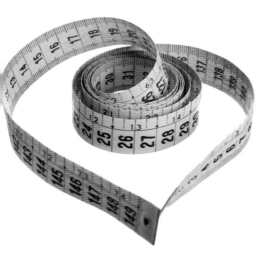

My meeting with Shaw proved to be a turning point in my battle of the bulge since he recommended a gastric bypass operation. He also said he thought a gastric band could be considered but in his opinion a bypass would be best. Now this wasn't easy to take… I wasn't a fat kid (indeed at times in my life I have been skinny), surely there was another diet around the corner that would work for me and hey, wasn't a bypass a bit drastic? A gastric bypass operation is a one-way ticket, there is no turning the clock back. What I was seduced by however, was the chance to press the 'reset' button and have another go at getting things right. I knew it wouldn't be the magic wand solution it is often portrayed to be by those who are ill-informed or mistaken, I would have to work at this new way of eating and use the surgery as a tool for that success. There would be no cast-iron guarantee unless I made changes and put in the work to eat mindfully.

In my efforts to find out more about the surgery itself and eating pre and post op, I explored websites, ordered books by the dozen, enrolled on forums and joined support groups. The conclusion I came to was that alright, there was a lot of information out there but little of it was grouped in a concise or constructive way. The biggest downfall for the patient was the lack of reliable advice and recipes geared to the UK market. Plenty for the Americans, but these had recipes that used unfamiliar and unavailable ingredients for the UK shopper; used cup and quart measures that again were confusing; and were geared and suited to the American palate. So my quest for a slimmer body quickly joined the desire to write the first UK book for weight-loss patients.

I don't believe you can write such a book unless you have travelled the weight-loss surgery journey yourself – and experienced the highs and lows of eating in a different way. Each day, after my surgery (because yes I did go ahead in November 2009), there has been a new challenge to eat wisely, cook well and nourish my body. This book has been developed and written from the experiences of my journey to date. I am still a 'work in progress' but I am some five stone (70 lbs) lighter, in just seven months.

It is now my aim to pass on all that I have learnt and will continue to learn – through this book and also my website **www.bariatriccookery.com**. I hope the website will be a continuation of this book (see page 105 for details). I also hope you'll join me and see how I and other weight-loss surgery patients are getting on food-wise in this brave new world!

Foreword by Shaw Somers

Food is central to everyone's life. In the main, we enjoy food as sustenance, comfort and entertainment! However, for some, food takes on a different association. Living with obesity, and regular dieting can spoil a person's relationship with food. Sometimes the enjoyment of food, followed by the guilt of having eaten can ruin an otherwise happy lifestyle. This can lead to significant distress and helplessness, and eventually feeling resigned to being big.

Over the years, treatments for overweight people have evolved into more applicable and acceptable measures. With the development of keyhole surgery less than 20 years ago, surgery to help weight control has become accepted by both the Medical profession and the public.

Surgery for weight loss involves one of three mechanisms: reducing appetite, reducing the ability to eat, and reducing food absorption. Most of the common operations will work by one or two of the above mechanisms.

The most popular operation is gastric banding. This involves placing an inflatable plastic ring around the upper stomach to restrict the passage of food. It will slightly reduce appetite, but doesn't change the absorption of foods – so inappropriate foods with high Calories will still be absorbed. Gastric bands work best for those who enjoy big meals, but rarely snack.

Gastric Bypass surgery is thought to be the most complete surgical procedure for weight loss. It involves stapling a small pouch of stomach for swallowed food to enter. The food is then re-directed into the intestine without passing through the main stomach. This causes a loss of appetite, restriction of eating, and a small amount of malabsorption (especially of sugars). It suits a wider variety of people, especially those with a sweet tooth or a snacking, irregular meal habit.

surgery isn't a complete cure, and some will need to... make lifestyle changes

There are more techniques being devised as time goes on, and each has particular pros and cons. My job as a specialist is to listen carefully to an individual patient's story and assess their lifestyle habits and evaluate their needs. I then try to match their individual requirements to the best operation for them. It is really important to get this part right, as the wrong choice of operation can result in either little weight loss or an even worse problem with food.

fearful that they will never eat normally after bariatric surgery. However, by following some straightforward guidance, relatively normal eating can be resumed. Just much less and savoured more slowly. I am so pleased that Carol has written this book; I hope it helps many people re-kindle their enjoyment of food after bariatric surgery.

Of course, surgery isn't a complete cure, and some will need to continue the battle against weight by sensible eating and lifestyle changes. Surgery simply helps to re-inforce the dietary changes and makes them easier to accomplish. For most, it is all the help they need to lead a happier life.

Bariatric surgery is fast becoming a routine surgical procedure. In fact, in the USA these operations are now more common that appendicectomy! The UK is following suit, and soon we will have a very significant number of people who will be living with the changes of lifestyle that Bariatric Surgery can bring.

it is really important that after surgery, patients feel confident about cooking enjoyable foods

Aside from simple weight loss, bariatric surgery can help to restore a more normal relationship with food and even enhance enjoyment and appreciation of flavours. For this reason it is really important that after surgery, patients feel confident about cooking enjoyable foods that work with their operation! I know that many are

Mr Shaw Somers BSc(Hons) MD FRCS
Consultant Specialist Upper Gastro-Intestinal and Bariatric Surgeon

From the commencement of registrar training at St Mary's Hospital, London, I have developed a specialist interest in upper gastrointestinal surgery. Working as lead clinician I have a comprehensive experience of complex upper GI surgical problems and lead one of the South of England's foremost Upper GI Surgical Units. I have extensive experience of Laparoscopic (Keyhole) surgery and have **performed over 3,000 procedures**.

Over the last 8 years I have developed and managed one of the most successful practices of Obesity Surgery in the South of England. **The Obesity Surgery Unit at St Richards Hospital, Chichester** has experience of over 2,000 bariatric cases and employs a full multidisciplinary team for patient care. The Unit performs over 500 obesity procedures per annum for both NHS and Private patients. I have developed new techniques for managing failed or complicated Bariatric procedures and am one of the few 'revision' surgeons in the UK. Recently, in partnership with **BMI Healthcare**, I have established a Bariatric Surgical Service in London.

The fat of the land

Across the land, in newspapers and magazines, on television and radio, in journals and research papers, in hospitals and boardrooms (especially where funding is being considered), the word obesity is increasingly being raised. Why? Well at its simplest, it is on the increase and massively so. Indeed so much so that a Government Report (the Foresight Report 1997), highlights the continuing problems the UK will face if we do not tackle obesity and its rapid rise. This discussion is also taking place globally across much of the developed world.

Current population data for the UK suggests that 22.1% of men and 22.8% of women are obese and that if these demographic trends continue, these are predicted to rise to 60% and 50% respectively by 2050. The impact of this on an over-stretched health service cannot be over-emphasised. The severe complications associated with obesity, such as Type 2 diabetes, arthritis, high blood pressure and heart disease, will put an enormous strain on the health of the nation as well as the individuals suffering from it. Depression and physical disability are also secondary ailments linked to this condition.

Obesity used to be a problem primarily faced by adults, but now we also see that children are starting to face the same obesity issues relating to health, like Type 2 diabetes, high blood pressure and raised cholesterol.

What is obesity?

At the very simplest level, obesity is defined as a BMI (Body Mass Index) of over 30. The BMI is a common measure of obesity that provides a comparison of an individual's weight in relation to their height and is strongly associated with body fat percentage.

So what causes it?

The actual cause of obesity is much more complicated than just an energy imbalance between energy taken in as food and energy expended out. Many other criteria come into play that are determined by the interaction and play between genetic, sociological, technological and individual motivators.

Genes are thought to be responsible for up to 70% of a person's weight gain. These control factors as diverse as appetite, satiety (a sense of fullness) and metabolism with all the complexities they involve. Factor-in the vagaries of will-power, choice, lifestyle and food availability and you have the makings of a very challenging and complex scenario to the behaviour patterns resulting from them.

Anyone who has struggled with their weight will recognise that all of these have a part to play in their weight management and that there is not a 'one size fits all' solution.

One thing that research has shown us however is that diets often fail. Only a mere 5% of dieters lose their excess weight and keep it off long-term. The remaining 95% often yo-yo between one diet and the next, each time increasing their starting weight by yet more pounds.

The implications of obesity

Not surprisingly there is a highly relevant link between a high BMI and increased morbidity. At its simplest, obesity is highly disabling and can result in premature death. Factor in the co-morbidities, like diabetes, and you can see that life can be shortened considerably by some few years.

The cost of obesity therefore on the individual is very significant, but it is also costly to the nation. The economic costs through loss of work, additional healthcare needs and incapacity benefits for those too ill to work are rising significantly.

The solution?

There are as many solutions as there are diets. For some the final option is bariatric (weight-loss) surgery. For those who have tried the usual and conservative methods of weight-loss without success, surgery may be the only solution.

Bariatric surgery is known to be the most effective and long-lasting treatment for morbid obesity (BMI 40+) and many related conditions. There is also mounting evidence to suggest that it may be among the most effective treatments for metabolic diseases and conditions, including obstructive sleep apnoea, high cholesterol, non-alcoholic fatty liver disease, hypertension and Type 2 diabetes.

Surgery for the morbidly obese goes way beyond weight-loss, for not only are the co-morbidities above improved, but joint disease, asthma and fertility can also be dramatically improved or resolved.

Bariatric surgery can typically lead to 50% of excess weight-loss over 5 years. For gastric bypass patients this can be higher, up to an average of 65-70%.

Bariatric surgery

Bariatric (weight-loss) surgery, be it gastric band, gastric bypass, gastric sleeve or duodenal switch, is only the start of the solution to obesity, for once you have had the operation the real work begins. The surgery itself is simply a tool to help and assist with weight-loss.

After the procedure and recovery period, you will need to work hard on developing new coping skills, learn an entirely new way of eating, address any emotional issues that still remain, work out how to break away from destructive patterns of old that hamper success, and consider the benefits of exercise to get moving for a better life. In short, many aspects of your life will have to change. Anyone who thinks the surgery itself is a 'magic wand' is sadly mistaken. Those who criticise the weight-loss surgery patient for taking 'the easy option' or who consider it to be 'cheating' are equally deluded. Surgery is just the beginning, what you do afterwards is the real key to success.

This isn't a book about the types of surgery on offer, for those who want to know more, go to some of the websites recommended on page 104, but please do your research (that way you will make the best decision for yourself). No, this is a food and recipe book to help maximise your success and results after surgery.

Alongside this book and its associated website, **www.bariatriccookery.com** you might like to also consider support groups and forums. It has been shown that those patients who participate have far better outcomes. Likewise the same is said for those who keep a food diary – keeping a check on the foods, portions and nutrients they have.

Waist disposal – exercise after surgery

Eating right is only half the battle and every health professional says it is important to also getting moving more. Weight-loss without exercise is slower and you are less likely to reach your goal weight.

Follow your own bariatric team's advice for when to start exercising after surgery for best and safe results. Once you are cleared, start slowly and try out anything that appeals. The best exercise is the one that you will do. It is pointless in taking out an expensive gym membership if you don't go.

I found it best to start simply by just walking a bit more – around the garden, up and down the stairs, around the neighbourhood and finally on the treadmill. Don't be intimidated by workout programmes – there are umpteen for absolute beginners to the advanced. The goal is to just get moving!

Make positive changes too in your ordinary day to day activities – I now park well away from the supermarket doors so that I have to walk a bit further; I get off the bus a stop earlier to give myself a bit more exercise; and take the stairs instead of the lift or escalator when out shopping. They are small steps but they build up quickly into something more measurable.

If you have difficulty in walking or weight-bearing for any length of time then consider a regime that can be done from a chair or having a swim.

Cooking after surgery

There is little doubt that if you cook for yourself then you are in control of what you are eating. It is one of the best things that you can do for yourself. It enables you to choose the best and freshest of ingredients, add only those foods that are nutrient rich, avoid those that are high in fat and sugar (and some nasty additives too) and limit your portion to an ideal size.

It may mean that you start to cook in a different way – you may grill, steam, poach, bake, braise, sauté and slow-cook more, at the expense of frying or adding rich sauces. It is hoped that the recipes that follow in the book are a springboard to get you started.

There are recipes for every stage of eating – some simple for mid-week eating and some designed more for entertaining or weekend meals; some for eating on your own or as a twosome, others for family gatherings; some lunchbox ideas or food that can travel and some, like the pizza recipe that has to be eaten straight from the oven. I hope I have also considered costs, seasonality and economy as well as some ideas for preparing well ahead and stashing in the freezer.

Bon appétit!

Stocking up on the best ingredients

There are some staples that the well-stocked bariatric kitchen shouldn't be without. They will help you to keep your dishes and choices wise when cooking and eating. Some can be used to conjure a meal up from nowhere when time and options are limited and others will add a touch of luxury when entertaining or making the most of a small portion. Manufacturers and producers are constantly launching and withdrawing food lines so only those with good availability are listed here unless they have an exceptional quality.

These are the foods that will supplement the fresh items in your shopping basket and are in addition to a well-stocked herb and spice rack.

It should be noted that certain foods can cause problems for some and yet not for others e.g. some WLS (weight-loss surgery) patients show an intolerance to artificial sweeteners which can cause 'dumping syndrome' (see page 30). Try a recipe with a low level of such an ingredient before even thinking about sampling one with a high level.

Canned, tubed and bottled foods:

Beans (kidney, black, cannellini, flageolet, butter and low-sugar baked)
Chickpeas (in salted water)
Olives (green and black)
Custard (low-fat and low-sugar)
Coconut milk (reduced-fat)
Evaporated milk (light)
Tomatoes (chopped in juice)
Soy sauce
Consommé or broths (low-fat)
Worcestershire sauce
Capers
Horseradish and mint sauce
Mustard (Dijon, English and wholegrain)
Tomato ketchup (low-sugar)
Tomato purée (double-concentrated)
Tomato sauce and salsa (low-sugar)
Vinegars (all types)
Vanilla extract or vanilla pods
Mayonnaise (extra-light)
French dressing (low-fat)
Oils (all types)
Cooking sprays (low-fat)
Pickles (low-sugar like onions, gherkins and dills)
Tuna and salmon (in oil or brine)
Pilchards and sardines (in brine or light tomato sauce)
Lime and lemon juice
Tahini paste
Tapenade
Tom yum Thai paste (for soup)
Umami paste (Laura Santini's No 5 paste)
Rose harissa paste
Pesto sauce
Thai red and green curry paste
Low-sugar squashes and cordials
Honey (clear)

Packets and cartons:

Lentils (green, red and Puy)
Wholewheat pasta (spaghetti and shapes)
Basmati and wholegrain rice
Dried apricots
Jellies (sugar-free)
Passata ('creamed' tomatoes)
Muesli (low-sugar)
Porridge oats
All Bran cereal
Unsalted nuts and trail mix
Cornflour
Ratafia biscuits
Melba Toast
Splenda granulated sweetener
Cocoa powder (unsweetened)
Stock cubes
Deli or tortilla wraps (low carb, traditional or multi-grain)
Multi-grain crispbreads and bread sticks
Wholemeal pitta breads
Hot chocolate drink (low-fat and low-sugar)
Skimmed milk powder

Chilled and dairy foods:

Milk (skimmed and semi-skimmed)
Cheddar (low or half-fat)
Baby Bel Light
Parmesan
Mozzarella (low or half-fat)
Ricotta (low-fat or fat-free)
Cream or soft cheese (low-fat)
Cottage cheese (low-fat)
Soya milk (unsweetened)
Yogurt (low-fat and low-sugar)
Greek yogurt (fat-free 0%)
Eggs
Egg whites (Two Chicks free range liquid)
Butter
Spreads (low-fat)
Crème fraîche (half-fat)
Whipped cream (low-fat)
Laughing Cow light cheese wedges
Halloumi and feta cheese
Hummous (reduced-fat)
Quark

Chilled or frozen foods:

Fish steaks and fillets
Minced beef, lamb and pork (extra lean)
Minced chicken and turkey
Chicken and turkey thighs and breasts
(skinless)
Beef, pork and lamb fillets or tenderloin
Prawns and shrimps
Scallops
Dressed crab
Thin deli-sliced lean meats like ham,
chicken and turkey
Smoked fish fillets
Frozen peas, sweetcorn and stir-fry mixes
Quorn mince and pieces
Bacon (traditional and turkey rashers)
Frozen fish pie mix
Frozen raspberries and summer fruits mix
Tofu

Special foods that are ideal for WLS patients:

Protein whey isolate powders (flavoured
and unflavoured, low-fat and low-carb)
Ready-prepared protein drinks (low-fat
and low-carb)
Crystal Light lemonade crystals
Low-carb tortilla wraps

Ten tips of advice from a dietician

- Follow the three stages of eating after surgery – Fluids, Soft Foods then Foods for Life. Don't progress onto the next stage until you are comfortable with the current one.

- Chewing well is the key to good progress and nourishment from the start. Initially cut food into very small pieces and chew at least 25 times. As time progresses the piece size can increase but you will still need to chew thoroughly.

- Relax and savour the flavour of the food. Mealtimes should still be a pleasant experience with family and friends.

- Mealtimes shouldn't last more than 25-30 minutes. Don't eat to satiety, allow time to pass and then go back for more. This grazing pattern only leads to over consumption of food.

- It is recommended that you eat three meals a day with two healthy small snacks. Remember to measure and weigh your food so that you are aware of the portion size you are eating.

- Protein is the major nutrient for consideration after weight-loss surgery along with a low-fat and low-sugar regime. However, do eat a good variety of foods and well-balanced meals. Protein should be your prime concern but not the only one.

- After gastric band surgery aim for 50-60g protein per day; after a bypass or gastric sleeve aim for 60-70g per day; and after duodenal switch aim for 80-120g per day. Not meeting this need can lead to protein malnutrition as well as hair loss.

- Consume enough liquid between meals to satisfy your thirst and prevent dehydration. Six to eight 250ml glasses of non-calorific, decaffeinated liquids are recommended each day as a minimum. Do not drink immediately before, during, or after meals.

- Don't forget to take your multi-vitamin, calcium supplement and any other medications you might be prescribed. Follow these up with blood tests recommended by your bariatric team or GP.

- **LEARN TO COOK** – that way you can control your food intake, know just what you are eating and still have a good, healthy relationship with food.

Weights and measures

I can't emphasise enough that getting organised and being well-prepared is all with this new way of eating. The new regime is much easier to follow if your store cupboard, refrigerator and freezer are ready for it; your kitchen has the gadgets to make light work of food preparation; and you have some fabulous, tried-and-tested advice for cooking and eating at your fingertips. Previous pages have given you the low-down on stocking up, now here are the hints and tips on preparing food, cooking it and eating of course!

Basic kitchen equipment

You won't need anything really special to get started but some pieces of equipment really do save the day, cut down on the hassle and are worthy of investment.

Kitchen scales: fairly obvious really to make sure that quantities are right and that you are not over or under-estimating how much a food or portion weighs. Mine ingeniously enable me to push a button and zero before adding the next ingredient.

Ice cube trays and small freezer boxes: an ice cube tray was one of the first gadgets I used before surgery to make some soups and puréed meals for when I came home. Simply make a batch of the food, pour into the tray, freeze until firm, then pop out into a freezer bag for long-term storage. Most cubes hold about 1 tbsp of food so you can remove a cube or three at a time to reheat depending upon your stage of eating. Likewise a good selection of small freezer boxes with lids will prove invaluable, although you could be thrifty and re-use yogurt pots and the like. Always label or you may get a surprise meal or two.

A food processor or blender: will make light work of soups for example, but is invaluable in those early post-surgery days for making nourishing drinks and smoothies. A small baby or single-portion-sized one (often sold as ideal for preparing babies' and toddlers' meals) is perfect for puréeing meals for the soft-food stage when quantities are still very small and smooth textured food is the order of the day.

Non-stick cookware and bake-o-glide: both of these negate the need for lashings of oil or butter to prevent food from sticking when grilling, baking or roasting. I constantly use my sheets of bake-o-glide and they seem to last forever. Dishwasher friendly, they also cut down on baked-on cookware that needs soaking to get clean again. I buy the one in a roll and cut to size for dishes, baking trays and tins but you could buy the ready-cut assortment.

Likewise my non-stick frying and sauté pan have become indispensable for making protein-rich omelettes and dry-frying fish, chicken and meat fillets with just a spritz of low-fat cooking spray.

Small ramekins: are the perfect dishes for cooking small meals and puddings in but also storing away the same in the refrigerator or freezer. Mine can also be used in the microwave, which makes storing, cooking and serving a one-stop operation and they look elegant too!

Zip-lock bags: these clever little bags enable you to store foods in an airtight fashion. I use them to freeze foods, store foods in marinades in the refrigerator and transport 'wet' items for a lunchbox treat. Most can be washed and reused with care and I have even snipped off the corner of one or two to make an instant piping bag!

Specialised kitchen equipment

I have a cupboard and shed full of gadgets and so anything that gets work surface space has earned it. Items I couldn't do without include:

Tefal Actifry: I just love this machine and I know countless other WLS patients who feel the same because we swap recipes and ideas for using it. It is the gadget that found fame by being able to fry a family-sized batch of chips with just 1 small spoonful of oil. The chips produced are crisp, golden and every bit as good (and nutritionally better) than those from the local chip shop. Fat levels for crisp-fried foods are cut to just 3%. I use mine to make other kinds of chips that are lower in Calories and carbs, for stir-frying vegetables, cooking lean cuts of fish, poultry and meat without oil, risottos and 'roasting' fruits for pudding.

A bento or tiffin lunchbox: again not an essential but my boxes enable me to separate my snacks from my main meal and my savoury from my 'sweetish' at the office or when I'm on the road. I also have a special little box of non-perishables in my car boot so that I don't get caught out by delays and traffic problems when away from home.

Electric ice cream maker: I bought my chef-type one off a friend and certainly wouldn't have paid the full three-figure price for it. However I have seen other domestic models that work just as well for a fraction of the price. An ice cream, sorbet or granita made in a machine this way always has a superior texture to one made by hand. I make lots of frozen ices so justify the outlay to myself. Checkout auction websites for a bargain if you think you will make good use of one.

Silicone poach pods and muffin trays: not essential by any means but a real bonus for poaching eggs, baking frittatas and even small cakes and muffins. The muffin trays are also the perfect size for holding a portion of casserole, curry or other savoury dish – freeze in the tray, pop-out when frozen and store in a freezer bag for ready-prepared meals when time is short (ideal for freezing a leftover portion of a meal or larger quantity batch-making of meals).

Cooking tips

I have been cooking and writing cookery features for some 35 years so could write a whole book about tips for cooking. Many of these I will pass on via my website **www.bariatriccookery.com** but here are some of the most useful that I have discovered after weight-loss surgery.

Variety is the spice of life: most herbs, spices and seasonings have almost no Calories but lift a dish immeasurably. The simplest omelette, fillet of fish or plain yogurt can be given a kick with a snip of fresh herbs, sprinkle of spice or dash of seasoning. I use fresh and dried herbs, a whole host of basic and exotic spices, and have a cupboard full of seasonings like Tabasco, Worcestershire sauce and many favoured vinegars, all the better for splashing onto or into a dish.

Lighten up: I still cook with a little butter and olive oil when the flavour is essential but for a lot of dishes I use a low-fat spray. The Calorie count and fat levels are reduced appreciably. I use a variety – sunflower oil and olive oil being the most popular.

Likewise I also use low-fat spreads in some recipes where they give a good result. Many manufacturers do not recommend them for cooking but I have had a good degree of success when sautéing quickly. If I have used them in a recipe then you can be sure it will work.

Pastes and sauces: there are so many good pastes and sauces out there that are low in fat and sugars that I don't hesitate in using them rather than starting from

scratch. I rely heavily upon ready-prepared Thai and Indian curry pastes, Moroccan harissa paste, tapenades, soy sauce, mustards and tomato purées but always check the nutritional labels first to make sure they are bariatric friendly.

Lazy helpers: again a visit to my refrigerator would reveal many a lazy ingredient that makes shopping, cooking and food preparation a joy. I unreservedly recommend lazy chopped or puréed garlic, chillies, lemon grass, root ginger and the like for countless dishes. As they say, life is too short…

Egg substitutes: the Americans go in for these big time but we can only find them in specialist stores so I don't tend to use them in recipes for everyone to share. However, I know a few WLS patients who are prone to problems with egg yolks, so, for them, I recommend Two-Chicks egg whites that can be purchased nationally from many supermarkets. They make fabulous egg white omelettes and frittatas and can be used wherever an egg white is required.

Service!

Use a smaller plate: I don't always, but often do, use a smaller plate for my meals at home. A side or salad plate proves to be just the right size. Choose an attractive one that makes a mealtime seem special. Sometimes I also use a smaller knife, fork and spoon too. If you have a tendency to rush your food, then try eating it with chopsticks to curb your speed.

Pace yourself: when eating with others who are eating normal-sized portions follow their pace so that you don't finish well ahead. If you think you are galloping ahead, put down your knife and fork and take a breather or chew your next mouthful especially well and slowly.

Go off menu or think outside the box: there is no written rule to say that you have to have a starter, main course then pudding. I often choose two starters when out dining instead of a starter and main course, rarely have (or share) a pudding or select cheese instead. You are also fully entitled to ask about what is in a dish and to ask them to hold off on an ingredient or serve it on the side e.g. hold the dressing or serve the sauce on the side.

For the brave (I'm one of them), ask for a child's portion!

Vital vitamins and nutritional supplements

Regardless of your surgery type your bariatric team will advise on taking a multi-vitamin and maybe some other supplements for the rest of your life. Why? Well, first of all, you're eating far less. Before your surgery, you were able to eat larger quantities of food, so you were probably getting most of the vitamins and minerals you needed from the food you ate. Now with your smaller stomach pouch you're undoubtedly eating less and so cannot get all the nutrients you require from your daily food intake. If you also underwent one of the malabsorptive surgeries (like the Roux-en-Y gastric bypass, for example), you're also not absorbing your vitamins and nutrients from food as efficiently as before, so an additional reason to reinforce the need for a regular daily supplement and long-term regime.

Your own bariatric team will advise you specifically on what you individually need so always follow their advice, however here is the general advice:

Multi-vitamins and supplements after a gastric band

With this type of surgery you do not have altered absorption of nutrients, so, if you are following a healthy diet, you should not become deficient in any vitamins and minerals. You will get most of your calcium requirements if you have three portions of dairy food in your diet each day (one portion = 200ml milk, a match-box size piece of cheese or 1 pot of yogurt, for example). However, whilst you are losing weight you might like to take one multi-vitamin tablet daily and perhaps a calcium supplement if meeting your requirements with dairy foods proves too challenging. Choose ones that can be broken up into smaller pieces to swallow so that they do not become stuck in your band stoma.

Alternatively, choose a chewable or liquid version, but avoid the capsule formulations. You might also want to ask your pharmacist about any existing medication you take to see if it is available in liquid form.

Multi-vitamins and supplements after a gastric bypass

After a gastric bypass it is very important to take additional vitamins as you are no longer able to absorb sufficient amounts of them from your food. Vitamin and mineral deficiency is an avoidable complication. Unfortunately, vitamin levels are hard to detect accurately in the body and you could become deficient before you show signs or symptoms of being so. As always, prevention is better than cure. Undoubtedly the best source of vitamins and minerals is a healthy diet, so eat mindfully with a good variety of foodstuffs. Most bariatric teams recommend a multi-vitamin tablet and a calcium supplement daily. Sometimes additional iron may be prescribed if your routine blood tests show you are becoming anaemic. Again you can choose chewable or liquid versions.

Multi-vitamins and supplements after gastric sleeve

Most bariatric teams recommend the same vitamin and mineral regime as that for gastric bypass patients even though the surgery is different. See above.

Multi-vitamins and supplements after duodenal switch

Advice here is similar to that for gastric bypass patients but because there is a greater degree of malabsorption you may have to watch your protein intake and your uptake of vitamins A, D, E and K, as well as iron and zinc. Most dieticians will recommend you try and eat double the amount of protein usually recommended to compensate for this. In addition you will need to take a multi-vitamin tablet daily. This will cover many of the essential vitamins and minerals but there are others which you need to pay special attention

to in addition to this. A and D are very important fat soluble vitamins, and because you are not absorbing fats you will need to take a water soluble version. Many people take ADEK vitamins (generally three per day) to maintain a proper level. Calcium is the most important mineral to take after duodenal switch surgery. You must take about 1,500 – 2,000mg per day ideally in the form of calcium citrate (rather than calcium carbonate which is not so easily absorbed). Many duodenal switch patients are also prescribed potassium straight after surgery, but do not need them as time progresses. About 10% of patients will also need to take iron but your GP will advise if this is necessary.

Fluids for life

Dehydration is one of the most common issues after weight-loss surgery, and may be potentially life-threatening if untreated. If you think of your body as a car, fluids are the petrol on which it runs, and without it or not enough of it you're in trouble! For your body to function at its best, you must constantly replace any fluids lost by taking in more through beverages and foods. In the first weeks after surgery this can be a pretty tall order so you may well find that you are constantly sipping to try and get that recommended **2.5-3.5 litres** inside.

Water is your best friend but also consider well-diluted low-sugar squashes and cordials and flavoured waters with a very low sugar content. Make up ice lollies with the same or buy sugar-free varieties. Milk, skimmed or semi-skimmed, will also prove invaluable and supply protein too. Tea and coffee will count towards your tally but opt for decaffeinated, herbal or fruit versions. Fruit juices can be useful if their sugar content isn't too high but, for safety, dilute with water to avoid too high a sugar hit. Salty drinks like Oxo, Marmite or Bovril should not take up more than 1 serving per day.

Protein drinks, made from whey protein isolate, reconstituted with skimmed milk or water, can be a real bonus since they not only provide fluid but essential protein too. Look for ones that are low in fat and sugar.

There are some tell-tale signs of dehydration, be aware of them:

- dry, sticky mouth
- darker urine (darker than straw-coloured)
- headache
- decreased urination
- thirst
- dizziness or light-headedness

Of course drinking isn't the only way that you can take in fluids. Many foods like fruits, fish, vegetables, eggs, salads and milk have a high-water content. Ensure your diet is rich in variety and includes them…but most of all drink up!

Fluids to avoid after weight-loss surgery

Carbonated or fizzy drinks: these can cause bloating and in severe cases can help stretch the new pouch. In the early days they can also give problems relating to gas, chest pain or pressure, causing much discomfort. If you are faced with a fizzy fluid and have little choice but to drink it, add ice, swirl around to remove as many bubbles as possible before imbibing.

Alcohol: alcohol is one of the few substances absorbed directly from your stomach and, since you have a smaller one, this area becomes saturated with alcohol more quickly. Some surgeons say no to alcohol, some allow a little in the diet, others suggest 'mindful' caution. In general go very easy, alcohol contains empty Calories and too many at that, so you are not giving your body any good nutrition and it could hamper your weight-loss efforts long term. If you opt to drink alcohol then sip rather than gulp, avoid any that are carbonated and don't plan to drive or operate heavy machinery. In short you have become the 'cheap date'.

High sugar, caffeinated and/or energy drinks: many of these are promoted as health-giving drinks but in reality are anything but. Loaded with sugar they can cause 'dumping syndrome' for bypass patients. Many also contain large amounts of caffeine. Caffeine in large quantities can leave you at higher risk of dehydration so will affect all weight-loss surgery patients if taken in excess.

High-fat beverages and soups: high-fat liquids, particularly if very hot or very cold versus room temperature can cause 'dumping syndrome' among gastric bypass patients. Duodenal switch patients may also be at risk from loose stools due to impaired fat absorption. Even band and sleeve patients can suffer because the fat content of such a liquid delays stomach emptying, which could produce bloating and/or diarrhoea. Such fluids are also Calorie dense slowing down weight-loss. So avoid rich creamy soups, full-fat coffee offerings, thick, ice-cream smoothies, sweet hot chocolate drinks and the like.

Immediate post surgery/fluids

There are 3 basic stages of eating after weight-loss surgery, regardless of type. **'FLUIDS'**, the first, is often considered to be the most challenging. Many return home from surgery, still feeling a little uncomfortable, certainly tired, clutching their hospital guidelines and then hover in the kitchen unsure about what to eat or drink next.

So what to do? First and foremost, follow your surgeon and bariatric team's advice to the letter. Some surgeons will recommend clear then full fluids for just a few days after surgery, others for as long as 4 weeks. This is to minimise digestion, lessen the production of solid waste and ensure maximum healing of your new gastrointestinal system.

'CLEAR LIQUIDS', the sort you can see through and that will comfortably travel up a straw, are first on the agenda. They should be sipped slowly and never gulped. It is important to have enough of them to keep hydrated, which in reality means you will almost constantly have one at your side in the early days. It is important that some of them are 'nutritional fluids' to give you some nourishment.

Listed opposite are some typical good choices and you will find favourites among them. Everything does taste strange to begin with, often too sweet, so dilute with water or ice for a more acceptable concentration and flavour. It has to be said that variety helps here, ring the changes often so that boredom doesn't set in. Even though there is a limited choice, this is for a reason. They will maximise healing and you should only move onto the next stage when advised and ready to do so.

General guidelines are that you should aim for 2.5 to 3.5 litres per day. It will be very hard to achieve this at first but do try. Spread them out evenly. Everyone has different fluid requirements; the best way to check you are well hydrated is to look at the colour of your urine. If output is pale, you are drinking enough. If it is dark e.g. straw-coloured or darker or if there is little urine, you need to drink more.

The recommended fluid portion size at any time is usually considered to be less than 200ml. In the very early days this will seem like an enormous amount! Each drink is also best taken more than 1 hour apart.

NEVER HAVE FIZZY DRINKS.

Good choices of clear fluids

- water
- tea – warm traditional, fruit or herbal teas
- coffee – warm, ideally decaffeinated
- 'no-added-sugar' or 'sugar-free' squashes and cordials
- Bovril, Marmite or Oxo 'salty' drinks diluted well with hot water
- sugar-free ice lollies
- sugar-free jelly, made up as per pack instructions
- chicken, beef or vegetable bouillon/broth/consommé or clear soup
- a whey protein isolate fruit drink like Syntrax Nectar, made up with water – great for getting protein in the early days

In addition to a daily multi-vitamin and calcium supplement

It may seem like an age but you will reasonably quickly then move onto the **'FULL LIQUIDS'** stage which provides a little more variety and nutrition to your diet. This is a vital stage since it prepares your surgically-altered stomach for more food. This stage again can last just a few days or a few weeks according to surgical opinion. Always follow your own surgeon's time-line.

Full liquids are those that are considered smooth and pourable. Mix and match them with clear fluids for good hydration throughout the day. Taste and flavour may still be off skew but again variety is the key to moving sensibly through this stage and preparing your body for the next one. It does get better every day and good habits can be quickly established at this stage to reap dividends later.

Good choices of full liquids

- milk – skimmed, semi-skimmed, soya, almond and Flora Pro active
- milky chai type tea – lightly-spiced for added flavour
- unsweetened plain yogurt or yogurt without added sugar and fruit bits
- smooth cream-style (but not high fat) soups
- whey protein isolate drinks, warm, cold or icy made up with water or milk
- whey protein isolate powder mixed with water or milk and made into an ice cream (see page 95)
- mashed potato mixed with a little broth or gravy until thin and soup-like
- diluted fruit juice
- tomato or V8 juice – warm or chilled
- Oatly – oat-based milk drink

- Rice Dream original milk
- Slimfast shakes and soups
- home-made smoothies (but not too thick) and shop-bought ones e.g. Innocent Strawberry and Banana, diluted if necessary with water
- cocoa (made with 4g powder and 200ml semi-skimmed milk)
- smooth-type cup-a-soups
- Highlight/Options hot chocolate drinks
- home-made vegetable, fish or poultry soups, puréed until smooth and diluted to a smooth runny consistency
- low-fat and low-sugar custards
- very gently set egg custards

 NOTE: Recipes suitable for this first stage of eating are colour-coded red.

Medium term post surgery/ soft foods

If you do not experience any problems with the Stage 1 'Fluids' regime then you will quickly move onto the second stage which incorporates smooth, puréed, soft and then crispy food, typically called the **'SOFT FOOD'** stage.

This stage is typically followed for about 2-6 weeks after surgery, although again always follow your bariatric team's advice on when to start and when to move on.

Start slowly and make sure initially that your food choices are soft and loose – first stage baby food texture is what you are aiming for here. Progress to foods that can be easily crushed with a fork or mixed to a 'slurry' with milk, gravy or sauce. Don't be put off when something doesn't suit…try it again a few days later. Ironically some days something goes down easily and the next time it doesn't. Learn to listen to your body and its signals of satisfaction or upset.

You will still need to be aiming for at least 2 litres of liquids a day in addition to these small 'meals'. Don't drink for 30 minutes before and 30 minutes after and aim for 4-6 small 'meals' per day.

Eat slowly and as soon as you are full STOP EATING! Just one extra teaspoon of food can send your system into overload and there is no pleasant way of saying this…what went down will come back up or make you feel very uncomfortable! Remember your new stomach pouch is only about the size of an egg cup.

You may find it very convenient to freeze soft meals in ice cube trays for this stage. I found a stash of these, prepared before surgery, so helpful in the coming weeks. Meals in this form can be prepared quickly for serving, variety is ensured rather than the relentless round of the same-old and wastage is reduced to a minimum.

Listed overleaf are some good food choices for the 'Soft Food' stage. Introduce these foods gradually replacing them as the days progress with ones that have more texture and flavour. Try to have 3 meals per day (ramekin or small tea plate size).

Crispy foods, which will fall to bits in water, such as Melba Toast, crispbreads, cream crackers and bread sticks can also be introduced in the latter days of Stage 2. Chew them thoroughly until reduced to a smooth purée in your mouth. Don't mistake them for crunchy foods e.g. fruit and salad which would cause problems at this stage.

This is the stage I believe you really should start looking at preparing your own recipes from scratch, that way you know exactly what is in them. Many processed foods and ready type meals have hidden sugars and fats to make them taste good but can be a banana skin for the weight-loss surgery patient. Try a few simple recipes to begin with or become extra vigilant at deciphering the back of pack nutritional information of a food. You're aiming for low-fat (as a guideline less than 3% fat i.e. less than 3g per 100g listed). As for sugar, toleration levels vary dramatically, but I wouldn't venture beyond the 6-7g hit per portion. It is thought that at levels beyond 10-15g you have a strong likelihood of bypass 'dumping' syndrome and it won't hurt those with a gastric band or sleeve to keep their Calorie count and sugar level low.

Good choices of soft foods

- Weetabix, porridge, Ready Brek with plenty of skimmed or semi-skimmed milk to make a runny consistency
- mashed banana with a little yogurt if liked
- very soft cooked scrambled egg
- finely minced or puréed chicken or turkey in gravy
- puréed fish in a thin sauce
- puréed canned fish e.g. tuna, pilchards, salmon or mackerel in a thin tomato sauce
- soft and smooth low-fat pâté or spread
- plain low-fat cottage cheese
- puréed mashed potato and thin gravy
- puréed canned and very tender boiled vegetables such as carrot and cauliflower
- low-fat and low-sugar fromage frais
- light and smooth low-fat and low-sugar mousse made with milk
- warmed mashed potato mixed with grated low-fat cheese or low-fat cream cheese
- milky pudding such as tapioca, sago or rice but keep sugar to a minimum
- puréed cauliflower cheese in a low-fat cheese sauce
- puréed, thickened or soft piece vegetable and chicken soups
- puréed casserole and stew dishes of a thinnish consistency
- very gently cooked and soft plain omelette

- poached egg or a soft-boiled one
- soft beans, lentils and peas, puréed or mashed for a little texture
- thick fruit smoothies
- puréed avocado
- small portions of home-cooked or ready-prepared and puréed main dishes like cottage pie, shepherd's pie, fish pie, fish-in-sauce, mild chilli con carne or their vegetarian alternatives made with quorn
- low-sugar sorbets
- silken or smooth tofu
- crispy foods like crispbreads, Melba Toast, cream crackers and breadsticks

In addition to a daily multi-vitamin and calcium supplement

NOTE: Recipes suitable for this second stage of eating are colour-coded yellow. You can of course also have those colour-coded red too.

The future/food for life

Only when you are able to tolerate a good variety of foods from Stage 2, should you then move tentatively onto Stage 3...eating **FOOD FOR LIFE**. Typically this occurs between 8-16 weeks post-op but everyone is different and always follow the advice of your own bariatric team. This is really the stage at which you should be able to try and eat a variety of solid food, in small amounts. Try using a side plate or child's plate as a guideline for serving size.

Foods to begin with should have a soft and moist texture so may have to be served with a little sauce, salsa, dressing or gravy so they chew into a moist mouthful, although as time goes on a drier texture is encouraged for constriction and an ideal transition through the newly altered digestive system. These so-called 'slider' foods help in the early days but can mean that you are able to digest more at a later stage just when you are looking for 'satiety' and don't want foods to pass through the stomach or pouch too quickly. Gradually cut down on them as you progress from week to week.

This is not a diet with a beginning and an end, nor is there need for a rush to the tape to get to your 'goal weight', take it slowly, learn to recognise when you are full and satisfied and don't eat beyond that point of satisfaction. As time goes on gastric bypass and sleeve patients will learn to recognise this point and gastric band patients will certainly, in time, find their 'sweet spot'.

It makes good sense to cook meals for everyone in the family rather than separate ones for all at this point. Why be a slave to a new regime that will happily suit all? Everyone can benefit from the foods suitable here, **high protein, low fat and low sugar**. Add an extra accompaniment for those growing members of the family or a sweet treat from time to time to get an ideal balance.

The regime and some rules

High protein, low fat and low sugar is the mantra

- Always eat your **protein first** (the meat, poultry, eggs, fish etc) on your plate, then move onto the vegetables and fruit and finally the carbohydrate element – potatoes, rice, pasta etc.
- Choose **lean protein** with any visible fat removed (e.g. chicken skin); aim for **low fat** (you won't always manage it but again aim for less than 3g fat per 100g); and always opt for a **low sugar** version of a meal or foodstuff (the syndrome known as 'dumping' – see page 30, is thought to occur when you eat between 7 and 15g sugar in one hit).
- Eat 3 meals per day with a couple of small snacks if necessary. These should satisfy you. However beware of developing a 'grazing' eating pattern of small snacks throughout the day.

- Eat healthy, solid food. Soft food undoubtedly slips down more easily but you can end up eating more over the course of the day. If your food is drier and more solid you will generally eat less overall and stay fuller for longer.

- **Eat slowly** and stop as soon as you feel full. Take tiny bites and chew each piece 10-25 times. **Chew, chew, chew and chew** some more! Once you feel full STOP! Gone are the days when you need to clear your plate.

- Keep your fluid intake up. It is also a good idea not to drink immediately before, during or after a meal so that your stomach isn't full from fluids. Get into this habit as soon as you can of not taking food and fluids together.

- **Take your multi-vitamin, calcium and any other supplement everyday** religiously… they will ensure that you have the best chance of getting all the additional nutrition you require that may not be supplied from the reduced amount of food you are eating.

- The hardest nutrient to keep on track with is undoubtedly protein. Aim for 70g per day. Quite difficult to begin with and do consider a whey protein isolate powder if you consistently fall short.

A scoop of this powder in food or as a drink can quickly and efficiently provide 25g or a third of your requirements in one fell swoop!

Cautionary foods

There are some cautionary solid foods, which may not be tolerated in the short and long term. Proceed with caution when eating them:

- non-toasted bread, especially soft and white
- over-cooked pasta and boiled rice
- red meat with a fibrous texture like steak and chops
- stringy vegetables like green beans
- sweetcorn, pineapple and mushrooms with a toughened texture
- pips, seeds and skins from fruit and vegetables
- dried fruits
- no caution, just a straight NO to fizzy drinks and chewing gum (for life)

 NOTE: Recipes suitable for this third and final stage of eating are colour-coded green. You can of course also have those colour-coded red and yellow too.

Eating right with every bite

This cookbook and the recipes in it have been specifically designed and developed to help you at every stage after bariatric (weight-loss) surgery. There are recipes and advice for the first 'Fluids' only stage; the same for the second 'Soft Foods' stage; and finally more for the final stage of 'Eating for Life'. They have been colour coded to make identification and selection easy.

How to use this cookbook

 1st 'Fluids' stage

 2nd 'Soft Foods' stage

 3rd 'Eating for Life' stage

If the recipe has been colour-coded as suitable for your eating stage then it can be considered for your eating plan, although in some cases the WLS portion may need to be puréed before serving.

However, people's tolerances vary greatly; so while I may recommend an ingredient or a recipe as being appropriate for a specific stage of your diet progression, only you will know what foods you can tolerate and when you can best tolerate them.

In addition, you will find a nutritional analysis breakdown with every recipe.

It includes Calories, protein, carbohydrate and fat levels. All analyses are based on the normal or average portion size. Underneath is a guide to the weight-loss serving portion size. Obviously, if you are a post-surgery patient, you will be eating smaller portions than the analysed amounts, so you will be having fewer Calories and less protein, carbohydrate and fat.

Recipes are also coded for suitability for freezing by this symbol ❄ and for vegetarians by this symbol Ⓥ

This book has been based on my eating adventures and experiences after gastric bypass surgery but also heeding the advice and discussions from other WLS patients who have had gastric bands, gastric sleeves and duodenal switches at countless support groups and on forums. I have been fortunate that I have had almost no digestion problems from the word go but I am mindful that some people do experience very real problems with sensitivity to some foods.

If this is the case for you then don't be afraid to be flexible with the recipes. For example, if you find it difficult to tolerate beef then try substituting it with turkey or chicken instead. It will usually work just as well. This book is all about making the new way of eating work for you.

A final word of caution – gastric bypass patients may well be susceptible to **'dumping syndrome'**. This condition, which is characterised by bloating, nausea and abdominal pain, can be the result of eating too much sugar or fat in one hit. Sugar is often the main culprit. My best advice is to be proactive and become a relentless label reader, since sugar is found in some products that you would never expect. Sometimes it can also happen if you have a sensitivity to artificial sweeteners. Most people who have experienced it say it is so awful that they will do anything they can to avoid it happening again. Heed their warning and keep your sugar and fat intake low by eating right with every bite!

This book is all about making the new way of eating work for you

Soya chai early morning cuppa

Here is a wonderfully soothing and lightly-spiced chai tea, perfect for even the earliest of post-surgery days. You can use almost any kind of teabag to make it but Darjeeling is especially good. The unsweetened soya milk can be replaced with skimmed or semi-skimmed cow's milk if preferred.

Calories: 55
Protein: 2.8g
Carbohydrate: 0.6g
Fat: 1.7g

SERVES 1
WLS portion: ½ - 1

150ml water
1 teabag
1 tsp honey
2-3 drops vanilla extract
1 small cinnamon stick or ½ tsp ground cinnamon
½ tsp ground cardamom
pinch of ground ginger
1 clove
75ml unsweetened soya milk

1. Place the water, teabag, honey, vanilla extract, cinnamon stick or ground cinnamon, ginger and clove in a small pan. Bring to the boil and simmer for about 3 minutes.
2. Remove from the heat and add the soya milk. Cover and leave to stand for 2 minutes to allow the spices to flavour the tea.
3. Strain to remove the teabag, cinnamon stick and any large particles of spices. Serve while still warm.

Super crunchy muesli

Here is a really good muesli base that you can vary by topping with different fruits. The mixture is baked to make it really crunchy and will remind you to take your time and chew very carefully over breakfast. Try it plain with a little milk or natural yogurt or top with seasonal fruit like berries, sliced banana or stewed apple.

Calories: 153
Protein: 4.1g
Carbohydrate: 8g
Fat: 9g

SERVES 15
WLS portion: ½ - 1

50g wheat bran flakes
150g rolled porridge oats
25g All Bran
2 tbsp groundnut oil
250g trail mix

1. Preheat the oven to 200°C/gas mark 6.
2. Mix the wheat bran flakes with the porridge oats, All Bran and oil. Spread evenly onto a baking tray.
3. Bake for 10-12 minutes, checking frequently and stirring if necessary to prevent burning.
4. Remove from the oven, add the trail mix and stir well to combine. Spread evenly again and bake for a further 5 minutes.
5. Remove from the oven and allow to cool completely before storing in an airtight container. Serve with milk, yogurt or fruit if liked.

Meal in a glass

There are just some days when, especially just after surgery, you can't stomach hearty food, and a drink is just about all you can face early morning or even later in the day. Later, well post-surgery, you may just be on the run and want to get some nutrients in, even if consumed in the car from a sealed-up cup. A smoothie, or meal-in-a-glass may be the answer. The recipes below and opposite are undoubtedly delicious and, providing you don't have problems with fruit sugars, will keep you well nourished. The mango protein one is a favourite because it matches the need for protein nourishment with flavour.

Strawberry and kiwi smoothie

Place 3 large strawberries, 1 peeled and chopped kiwi fruit, 1 small sliced banana and 125ml chilled, skimmed cow's milk or unsweetened soya milk in a blender and process until smooth. Serve chilled.

SERVES 1
WLS portion: ½ - 1

Calories: 170
Protein: 6.2g
Carbohydrate: 28.6g
Fat: 3g

Summer berry and banana smoothie

Place 75g frozen summer berry fruits (raspberries, blueberries and redcurrants), 1 small sliced banana and 150ml skimmed milk in a blender and process until smooth. Serve chilled.

SERVES 1
WLS portion: ½ - 1

Calories: 160
Protein: 6.9g
Carbohydrate: 31.3g
Fat: 0.6g

Banana, honey and cinnamon smoothie

Place 1 small sliced banana, 150ml skimmed milk, 125g pot natural low-fat yogurt, 1 tbsp clear honey and a large pinch of ground cinnamon in a blender and process until smooth. Serve chilled.

SERVES 2
WLS portion: ½ - 1

Calories: 143
Protein: 6.5g
Carbohydrate: 26.8g
Fat: 1g

Mango protein smoothie

Place flesh of half a peeled and stoned mango, 1 scoop whey protein isolate powder (e.g. Syntrax Nectar Fuzzy Navel, see page 104 for stockist) and 150ml skimmed milk in a blender and process until smooth. Serve chilled.

SERVES 1
WLS portion: ½ - 1

Calories: 206
Protein: 28.5g
Carbohydrate: 24.5g
Fat: 0.4g

Protein smoothies: there is no doubt that it is better to get your protein from food rather than supplements. However, some of us just can't get the 70-100g recommended level on a daily basis and constantly fall short. This is where a protein drink can bridge the gap. One drink can supply about 24g protein! There are copious brands around and it is only by tasting that you will know if they hit the spot or not. I find many just too overly sweet. I really like the Syntrax Nectar range. Make up with milk for added protein and add a little frozen or fresh fruit to lift to a fresher level.

Brunch style Spanish omelette

This Spanish omelette is endlessly versatile. Serve warm at the weekend for a lazy Sunday brunch; with salad as a light mid-week entertaining lunch (perhaps in the garden); chilled and cut into wedges then packed into a lunchbox; or cut into small triangles as a perfect tapas style nibble.

Calories: 210
Protein: 14.4g
Carbohydrate: 19g
Fat: 8.9g

SERVES 2
WLS portion: ½ - ¾

100g new potatoes
Fry Light low-fat cooking spray
1 small onion, finely chopped
1 courgette, chopped
2 tomatoes, skinned and chopped
4 medium eggs
1 tbsp milk
2 tbsp grated Parmesan cheese
salt and freshly ground black pepper

1. Bring a pan of lightly salted water to the boil. Add the new potatoes, reduce the heat to a simmer and cook for about 15 minutes or until the potatoes are tender. Drain, leave to cool then cut into slices.
2. Spray a non-stick frying or omelette pan with Fry Light. Add the onion and cook for 2 minutes.
3. Add the courgette and sauté for a further 6 minutes.
4. Add the tomato and cook for 2 minutes, then stir in the sliced potatoes.
5. Meanwhile, beat the eggs with the milk, Parmesan and salt and pepper to taste. Preheat the grill to high.
6. Pour the egg mixture over the vegetables and cook, over a medium heat, for about 4 minutes, or until the eggs are set underneath.
7. Place the pan under the grill (with the handle sticking out if not metal) and cook for about 3 minutes until golden and set.
8. Serve warm from the pan or leave to cool, then cut into wedges to serve.

Thai chicken and vegetable soup

This is a chicken soup, flavoured with Thai ingredients, which is enriched and thickened with vegetables. It is an all-time favourite that freezes beautifully both chunky and smooth, I prefer the latter. High in protein, low in fat and sugar it is the perfect nutritious light lunch dish or starter. It was one of the first puréed dishes I tried after surgery and really hit the spot after bland-tasting liquids. If you are pre-surgery, why not make a batch and freeze away for those early post-surgery days when you may not feel like cooking.

Calories: 128
Protein: 15.7g
Carbohydrate: 7.6g
Fat: 4.1g

SERVES 4
WLS portion: ⅓ - ½

400ml can reduced-fat coconut milk
1 large onion, finely chopped
1 clove garlic, crushed (optional)
1 tbsp chopped fresh ginger
1 tsp chopped fresh chilli
1 tsp tom yum Thai paste (for soup)
600ml chicken stock
250g skinless and boneless chicken, diced
250g mixed diced vegetables (carrots, cauliflower, green beans and leek for example)
salt and freshly ground black pepper
chopped fresh coriander to garnish (optional)

1. Put the coconut milk, onion, garlic (if used), ginger, chilli and tom yum Thai paste in a large pan and mix well.
2. Add the stock, mixing well and bring to the boil. Reduce the heat and simmer, uncovered, for 20 minutes.
3. Add the chicken, vegetables and salt and pepper to taste. Cover and simmer for 1 hour.
4. Serve the soup chunky or purée until smooth in a blender, depending upon bariatric eating stage.
5. Garnish with chopped fresh coriander to serve if liked.

Boxing clever

Countless WLS patients have told me that they struggled to know what to eat in their lunchboxes after their ops. Sandwiches are often out and there is only so much couscous and rice salad that you want to eat. Here are a few ideas that travel well, are pouch-friendly yet can be made for all the family to enjoy.

Smoked salmon, cucumber and dill pâté

Chop 75g smoked Alaska salmon into small pieces and slice a further 75g into strips. Mix 400g extra-light soft cheese with 2 tbsp chopped fresh dill, the finely grated zest of 1 lemon, 1 tbsp lemon juice, a finely chopped quarter of cucumber and freshly ground black pepper to taste. Fold in the chopped salmon and place in a container. Top with the remaining strips of salmon and garnish with a few sprigs of dill. Serve with triangles of wholemeal toast or Melba Toast.

SERVES 4
WLS portion: ⅓ - ½

Calories: 182
Protein: 19.4g
Carbohydrate: 5.1g
Fat: 9.3g

Greek style pasta salad

Cook 225g dried fusilli pasta according to the pack instructions. Drain, reserving 2 tbsp of the cooking liquid. Toss the pasta with 50g Kalamati olive and sun-dried tomato tapenade and the reserved cooking liquid. Meanwhile, dry-fry 25g pine nuts until golden. Add to the pasta with 100g crumbled feta cheese, 100g chopped cucumber, 1 small sliced red onion and half a 25g pack of fresh basil, roughly shredded. Season to taste and toss well to mix.

SERVES 4
WLS portion: ½

Calories: 350
Protein: 13.2g
Carbohydrate: 45.4g
Fat: 12.4g

Caesar egg salad

Cook 6 large eggs until softly hard-boiled.
Shell and cut into quarters. Place one of
the eggs in a food processor with 4 tbsp
fat-free French dressing and purée until
smooth. Add a little boiling water if
necessary to mix to a coating consistency.
Mix the egg quarters with 1 shredded Cos
or Romaine lettuce, 25g grated Parmesan
cheese, a drained 50g can of anchovies
and the prepared dressing. If serving
immediately toss with a 20g pack Melba
toast, coarsely broken. If serving or eating
later then pack the Melba toast separately
and toss with the salad just before serving.

SERVES 4
WLS portion: ½

Calories: 200
Protein: 15.9g
Carbohydrate: 7.4g
Fat: 11.6g

Chicken, egg and watercress dip

Mix 3 finely chopped hard-boiled eggs
with 50g chopped watercress, 4 tbsp
extra-light mayonnaise and 75g finely
chopped, cooked, skinless chicken.
Season to taste and serve with pitta breads
and vegetable crudités if liked. Purée the
dip mixture if serving during the soft food
stage of eating.

SERVES 4
WLS portion: ½ - ¾

Calories: 98
Protein: 10.2g
Carbohydrate: 2.2g
Fat: 5.4g

Minted pea soup

This has to be one of my favourite soups, devised in the summer but eaten all year round. If you are concerned about or have trouble digesting pea skins then pass the soup through a coarse sieve before serving.

Calories: 102
Protein: 6.5g
Carbohydrate: 16.7g
Fat: 1.1g

SERVES 6
WLS portion: ½ - 1

Fry Light olive oil spray
1 onion, chopped
2 small potatoes, peeled and cut into small cubes
1 tsp garlic purée
5 tsp mint sauce
1 litre vegetable stock
450g frozen peas
salt and freshly ground black pepper
3 tbsp fat-free Greek yogurt
mint leaves to garnish
cheesy garlic croûtons to serve (optional)

1. Spray a large pan with Fry Light, add the onion and potatoes and cook until lightly browned.
2. Add the garlic, mint sauce and stock. Bring to the boil, reduce the heat, cover and simmer for about 15 minutes, or until the potato is tender.
3. Add the peas with salt and pepper to taste and simmer for a further 5 minutes.
4. Remove from the heat, allow to cool slightly, then purée in a blender, in batches, until smooth.
5. Divide between serving dishes, swirl the yogurt into the soup and garnish with mint sprigs. Serve with cheesy garlic croûtons, depending upon bariatric eating stage.

Comforting lentil soup

This easy-to-prepare lentil soup is infused with the flavour of red pepper and cumin and is very comforting in the early stages of recovery after surgery. It freezes beautifully so is well worth the effort of making in bulk.

Calories: 33
Protein: 8.2g
Carbohydrate: 22.2g
Fat: 1.5g

SERVES 6
WLS portion: ⅓ - ½

2 tsp oil
1 medium onion, chopped
1 clove garlic, chopped
1 medium red pepper, chopped
200g carrots, peeled and chopped
2 tsp ground cumin
150g red lentils
400g can chopped tomatoes
1750ml vegetable stock
salt and freshly ground black pepper
crispy toast croûtons to serve (optional)

1. Heat the oil in a large pan. Add the onion and garlic and cook for 4-5 minutes until softened.
2. Add the red pepper, carrots and cumin, mixing well. Cook for a further 2 minutes.
3. Stir in the lentils, tomatoes, stock and salt and pepper to taste. Bring to the boil, reduce the heat and simmer for 45-60 minutes until the vegetables and lentils are very soft and cooked.
4. Remove from the heat, allow to cool slightly, then purée in a blender, in batches, until smooth and creamy in texture.
5. Serve hot with a few crispy toast croûtons if liked, depending upon bariatric eating stage.

Wild Alaska salmon raita

This salmon raita is not only delicious with naan bread, crispbread or Melba Toast but makes a fabulous filling for sandwiches, wraps and pitta bread. It's worth making double the quantity – it will keep in the refrigerator for up to 2 days.

Purée and serve with crispbread

Calories: 116
Protein: 14.2g
Carbohydrate: 1.4g
Fat: 6g

SERVES 2
WLS portion: ½

160g can red or pink wild Alaska salmon
2 tbsp fat-free Greek yogurt
50g piece cucumber, chopped
1 tbsp chopped fresh coriander
salt and freshly ground black pepper

1. Drain the can of salmon, remove any skin and bones from the salmon and break into chunks.
2. Add the yogurt, cucumber, coriander and salt and pepper to taste, mixing gently. Chill until ready to serve.
3. Serve with warm naan bread (grilled for about 1 minute on each side) or your chosen variety of crispbread or Melba Toast.

All wrapped up

Wraps and pockets are the exciting new alternative to sandwiches and are surprisingly WLS patient friendly. Light on carbs and fats, tortilla wraps and pittas are the versatile and modern way to enjoy new high protein fillings for those with a busy lifestyle. Perfect for a light lunch they also travel well in lunchboxes providing good nutrition away from home. Choose wholemeal pittas for added fibre and low-carb tortillas or, as a back-up, regular versions with multi-grains. Stuff with a high protein mixture flavoured with a little sauce, salsa or dressing.

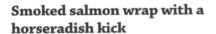

Smoked salmon wrap with a horseradish kick

Mix 2 tbsp extra light, low-fat soft cheese with 1-2 tsp horseradish sauce and salt and pepper to taste. Spread over a low-carb tortilla wrap. Top with 75g smoked Wild Alaska salmon, a few sprigs of watercress, a few thin slices of cucumber and radish if liked. Roll up tightly then slice in half to serve.

SERVES 1
WLS portion: ½ - 1

Calories: 207
Protein: 27.1g
Carbohydrate: 12g
Fat: 5.5g

Quorn lamb grill pittas

Cook a 178g pack lamb-style Quorn lamb grills according to the pack instructions then slice into thin strips. Warm 2 wholemeal pittas. Stuff with a little shredded lettuce, cucumber and tomato slices, red onion rings and Quorn strips. Drizzle over 2 tbsp tzatziki dressing and serve at once.

SERVES 2
WLS portion: ½ - 1

Calories: 300
Protein: 18.1g
Carbohydrate: 46.5g
Fat: 6g

Egg and tomato pitta pockets

Place 2 eggs in a pan of cold water. Slowly bring to the boil then simmer for 7 minutes. Drain, rinse in cold water, tap the shells to crack and leave to cool. When cold, peel away the shells and roughly chop. Mix with 2 tbsp extra light, low-fat mayonnaise, 2 chopped tomatoes and salt and pepper to taste. Divide the mixture between 2 wholemeal pittas, opened to make pockets. Wrap in greaseproof paper and chill until required.

SERVES 2
WLS portion: ½ - 1

Calories: 288
Protein: 14.5g
Carbohydrate: 41.7g
Fat: 8.7g

Rise and shine wrap: fill a wrap with thinly-sliced smoked ham, sliced hard-boiled egg, rocket or lettuce leaves, sliced tomato and a drizzle of low-sugar tomato ketchup.

Feel good healthy Caesar wrap: fill a wholewheat wrap with sliced chicken, sliced avocado, chopped spring onions, a sprinkling of Parmesan cheese and a drizzle of low-fat Caesar dressing.

Vegetarian delight: fill a herb wrap with cooked sweet potato, roasted peppers, a little crumbled feta cheese and a drizzle of sun-dried tomato pesto.

Christmas special: fill a multi-grain wrap with sliced turkey, little gem lettuce, a little red onion and a smear of cranberry sauce.

Fishy wrap: fill a wrap with cooked flaked salmon or tuna, shredded lettuce, a spoonful of cooked sweetcorn, a sprinkling of chives and a drizzle of low-fat Thousand Island dressing.

Mexican black bean wrap: mix mashed black beans, a little tomato salsa and a drizzle of reduced-fat sour cream in a bowl and microwave for 1-2 minutes to heat. Use to fill a wholewheat tortilla and serve at once.

Salad niçoise with beans and peas

This salad, made with tuna, eggs and the best of British fresh green beans and peas, is endlessly versatile. It makes a wonderful light summer lunch for friends and yet can be packed in a box for a desk-top lunch or picnic.

Calories: 220
Protein: 19.7g
Carbohydrate: 16.5g
Fat: 8.1g

SERVES 4
WLS portion: ½

200g new potatoes, halved
4 medium eggs
200g fresh green beans, trimmed
100g fresh peas, shelled
185g can tuna in brine, drained and flaked
12 black olives
4 anchovy fillets
1 small shallot, very finely chopped
5 tbsp fat-free French dressing
salt and freshly ground black pepper

1. Cook the new potatoes in boiling salted water until tender, about 15 minutes. Drain and set aside.
2. Meanwhile, cook the eggs in boiling water until just hard-boiled but not dry, about 7 minutes. Cool under running water for 5 minutes then shell, cut in half and set aside.
3. In the meantime, cook the beans and peas in boiling salted water for 2 minutes. Drain, lightly refresh under cold water then drain again.
4. Mix the potatoes with the eggs, beans, peas, tuna, olives and anchovies.
5. Mix the shallot with the French dressing and salt and pepper to taste. Pour over the salad mixture and mix gently to serve.

Crab and mango salad with lime and chilli dressing

This mouth-watering salad is quickly made if you buy fresh dressed crab from the fish counter in your supermarket. It is finished with a chilli and lime dressing made with a ready-prepared fat-free French dressing. You can however use your own home-made dressing – you'll need about 3-4 tbsp.

Calories: 135
Protein: 10.1g
Carbohydrate: 15g
Fat: 4.5g

SERVES 4
WLS portion: ½

2 dressed crabs, about 130g each
1 medium ripe mango, peeled and sliced
½ cucumber, thinly sliced
10g fresh mint, chopped
100g watercress
3 tbsp fat-free French dressing
finely grated rind of 1 lime
juice of ½ lime
1 tsp chopped fresh red chilli
salt and freshly ground black pepper

1. Remove all the light and dark meat from the crab shells and place in a large bowl. Add the mango, cucumber, mint and watercress and toss gently to mix.
2. Place the dressing, lime zest, lime juice, chilli and salt and pepper to taste in a small bowl and whisk gently to blend.
3. Divide the salad between 4 plates and drizzle with the dressing. Serve at once.

Going solo and duo

One of the most frequent requests I receive is for some recipes that serve one or two. Just because you are dining solo or duo doesn't mean you can't cook something delicious from scratch and still have the makings of a great dining experience. Small measures and simple pleasures can mean that WLS patients are doing it enticingly for themselves!

Pollock and chorizo supper

Heat a wok or large frying pan and add 25g sliced chorizo. Cook for 1-2 minutes to release the flavours. Add 1 small crushed clove of garlic, half a bunch of sliced spring onions and 1 chopped red or yellow pepper. Stir-fry for 2-3 minutes to soften. Add a drained 400g can of mixed beans, 175g tomato and basil pasta sauce and 50g chopped fine beans, mixing well. Cook for 5 minutes. Add 200g diced Alaskan Pollock fillet and 6 halved cherry tomatoes and simmer for a further 5 minutes, without stirring. Season to taste and serve garnished with chopped parsley.

SERVES 2
WLS portion: ½ - ⅔

Calories: 395
Protein: 33.5g
Carbohydrate: 39.7g
Fat: 11.1g

Egg white omelette with ricotta and roasted peppers

Cook 120g watercress, spinach and rocket salad in a little water for 3-4 minutes. Drain well then chop finely. Whisk 150ml Two Chicks liquid egg white for 3-4 minutes. Whisk in the salad and season. Preheat the grill to high. Heat a non-stick frying pan and spray with Fry Light. Add the egg mixture and cook until the base has set. Transfer to the grill and cook for 2-3 minutes. Top with 100g ricotta cheese and 100g sliced roasted peppers to serve.

SERVES 1
WLS portion: ½ - ¾

Calories: 253
Protein: 28.5g
Carbohydrate: 6.1g
Fat: 10.6g

Quorn with hoisin noodles

Cook an 80g pack of dry egg noodles according to the pack. Drain well. Meanwhile, mix a 175g pack Quorn mince with 3 tbsp hoisin sauce, 1 crushed clove of garlic, 2 tbsp rice wine, 1 chopped red chilli and 1 tbsp soy sauce. Heat a wok and spray with Fry Light. Add 4 chopped spring onions and 50g halved mangetout and fry for 1 minute. Add 75g beansprouts and 125g chopped pak choi and fry for a further 1 minute. Add the Quorn mixture and fry for 2 minutes. Add the noodles and toss to mix.

SERVES 2
WLS portion: ½ - ¾

Calories: 338
Protein: 22.8g
Carbohydrate: 50.9g
Fat: 3.5g

Griddled turkey with salsa

Mix 1 tsp garlic purée with 1 tsp chopped rosemary and use to coat a 100g turkey steak. Marinate for 30 minutes. Meanwhile, mix 1 chopped tomato with 1 chopped spring onion, a little diced cucumber, 1 tsp sweet chilli sauce, 1 tsp lime juice and 2 tsp chopped coriander. Preheat a griddle until smoking hot. Spray the turkey with Fry Light, then griddle for 8-10 minutes until cooked. Serve with the salsa.

SERVES 1
WLS portion: ¾ - 1

Calories: 154
Protein: 26.4g
Carbohydrate: 9.7g
Fat: 1.5g

Yes, you can have pizza!

I thought my pizza days were over...until I started to try and improvise with something a little lower carb than a deep pan base and toppings that weren't so fat-laden. This is the end result...a pizza on a low carb or wholemeal tortilla with protein rich toppings that offer good nutrition. The secret is not to load too far in advance of cooking or the base goes soggy and to eat straight from the oven...no problem with that! This is my basic pizza but the variations are endless.

Calories: 245
Protein: 22g
Carbohydrate: 11.9g
Fat: 12.3g

VARIATIONS

All day breakfast: top with ham or cooked turkey rashers, cherry tomatoes, cheeses and 2 eggs cracked over the whole just before cooking.

Meat-free Monday: top with 100g ready-prepared grilled courgettes, peppers and aubergines in oil (drained well), tomatoes, cheeses and herbs.

Marinara: top with flaked tuna or salmon, tomatoes, cheeses, 2 tsp capers, 6 anchovy fillets and herbs.

Meat monster: top with ham or chicken, as above, plus 50g sliced chorizo, tomatoes, cheeses and herbs.

SERVES 2
WLS portion: ¼ - ⅓

1 low carb or wholemeal tortilla
2 tbsp tomato salsa
50g chopped ham, chicken or flaked tuna
6 cherry tomatoes, halved
125g low or half-fat mozzarella, thinly sliced
6 olives or anchovy fillets
1 tbsp chopped fresh herbs or a few basil leaves
1 tbsp grated Parmesan cheese
salt and freshly ground black pepper

1. Preheat the oven to 190°C/gas mark 5.
2. Lightly grease a baking tray or line with non-stick bake-o-glide. Place the tortilla on top.
3. Spread the tomato salsa evenly over the tortilla. Top with your chosen meat or fish, the cherry tomatoes, mozzarella, olives or anchovies, chopped herbs (if using basil, add after cooking), Parmesan and salt and pepper to taste.
4. Bake at once for exactly 10 minutes. Serve cut into wedges with salad if liked.

Herder's pie

This is a bariatric-friendly version of the popular Shepherd's Pie, made with beef instead of lamb. The topping also has a hefty portion of swede instead of potato which brings down the Calorie and carb level. It is however still hearty enough to cope with non WLS man-sized appetites for family eating!

Calories (without cheese): 337
Protein: 32.8g
Carbohydrate: 39.1g
Fat: 6.2g

VARIATIONS

Bobotie: add 1 tbsp curry powder to the mince mixture with the onion.

Beany herder's pie: add a 425g can low-sugar baked beans to the meat mixture before topping with the mash.

SERVES 6
WLS portion: ½

800g lean minced beef
1 large onion, finely chopped
2 large carrots, chopped
300ml passata
1 beef stock cube
3 tbsp Worcestershire sauce
salt and freshly ground black pepper
750g swede, peeled and diced
4 large potatoes, peeled and diced
4 tbsp grated low-fat cheese (optional)

1. Preheat the oven to 150°C/gas mark 2.
2. Cook the mince in a non-stick, ovenproof pan until browned. Add the onion and carrots and cook for a further 5-10 minutes until softened.
3. Add the passata, crumbled stock cube, Worcestershire sauce and salt and pepper to taste, mixing well. Cook for 5 minutes.
4. Cover and cook in the oven for 1 hour, then increase the oven temperature to 200°C/gas mark 6.
5. Meanwhile, cook the swede in boiling water until soft, then drain and mash to a purée. At the same time, in another pan, cook the potatoes in boiling water until tender, then drain and mash to a purée. Mix the swede with the potato until well combined.
6. Transfer the beef mixture to a large or 6 individual baking dishes and top with the swede and potato mash. Sprinkle with grated cheese if liked and bake for 20-25 minutes until browned. Serve with vegetables in season.

A right grilling...

It may be some time after weight-loss surgery before you can enjoy a burger or a kebab again but when you do, make sure it is full of flavour. The recipes here are bursting with flavour and lift ordinary meat or fish into the luxury category. The secret to their success and pouch friendliness is in serving them with a sauce or salsa which gives added moisture but do remember to chew, chew, chew!

Salmon, carrot and halloumi burgers

Preheat the oven to 200°C/gas mark 6. Mix 2 x 213g cans drained red or pink salmon with 500g grated carrots, 1 finely chopped small onion, 100g fresh breadcrumbs, 50g half-fat grated Cheddar cheese, 150g crumbled light halloumi cheese, 1 tbsp chopped fresh coriander, 1 beaten egg and salt and pepper to taste. Form the mixture into 6 burgers and place on a non-stick baking tray. Bake for about 20-25 minutes until golden brown. Alternatively, grill over a medium heat on a barbecue for 15-20 minutes, turning once. Serve with salad and in a bun if liked.

SERVES 6
WLS portion: ½ - 1

Calories: 263
Protein: 22.8g
Carbohydrate: 16.2g
Fat: 12.4g

Jerk pork and shallot skewers with pineapple salsa

Mix 3 tbsp jerk seasoning with 3 tbsp fat-free Greek yogurt. Add to 500g cubed pork loin steaks and 12 halved shallots. Marinate for at least 30 minutes. Mix half a small chopped pineapple with 3 finely chopped shallots, 3 tbsp chopped fresh coriander, the juice and zest of 1 lime and 3 seeded and chopped red chillies. Thread the pork and shallots onto skewers and cook under the grill or over a medium hot barbecue for 10-15 minutes. Serve with the salsa.

SERVES 4
WLS portion: ½ - ¾

Calories: 332
Protein: 32g
Carbohydrate: 19.5g
Fat: 14.6g

Minted lamb kofta

Mix 500g lean minced lamb with 50g breadcrumbs, 1 chopped onion, 4 tbsp chopped fresh mint, 1 beaten egg and salt and pepper to taste. Divide into about 16 balls and thread onto skewers. Grill for about 15 minutes. Mix 300ml fat-free natural yogurt with 2 tsp chopped fresh mint. Serve with the koftas in pitta breads if liked.

SERVES 4
WLS portion: ½

Calories: 320
Protein: 27.8g
Carbohydrate: 21g
Fat: 13.7g

Chilli con carne with avocado salsa

Here is a fabulous oven-baked chilli that could also be made with any number of other canned beans. Try black bean, blackeye or borlotti or a mixture for variety. Lovely served with rice and an avocado salsa.

 Purée

**Calories: 340
(including salsa)
Protein: 34.2g
Carbohydrate: 20.9g
Fat: 13.4g**

Avocado salsa: Mix the flesh of 1 ripe chopped avocado with half a small chopped red onion, 2 chopped tomatoes, the juice of half a lime and salt and pepper to taste. Serve sprinkled with chopped coriander if liked.

**SERVES 4
WLS portion: ⅓ - ½**

500g extra lean minced beef
1 onion, chopped
400g can chopped tomatoes in rich tomato juice
   or 500g carton passata
1 tbsp chilli and cocoa bean spice blend or
   1-1½ tsp chopped red chilli
2 tbsp ground paprika
1 tbsp Worcestershire sauce
1 beef or vegetable stock cube
salt and freshly ground black pepper
400g can red kidney beans, drained

1. Preheat the oven to 150°C/gas mark 2.
2. Crumble the beef into a non-stick, flameproof and ovenproof pan. Cook, over a high heat, until browned, stirring well.
3. Add the onion and cook for a further 5 minutes.
4. Add the tomatoes or passata, spice blend or chilli, paprika, Worcestershire sauce, stock cube and salt and pepper to taste, mixing well. Cover and cook for 5 minutes.
5. Transfer to the oven and cook for 1 hour.
6. Add the drained beans, mixing well. Cover and cook for a further 15 minutes. Serve with rice and avocado salsa if liked.

Lamb tagine

Tagine is the name for the distinctive shaped cooking pot found everywhere in Morocco where this dish is most popular. You can of course just use a casserole with a tight-fitting lid to cook this most flavoursome stew.

 Purée

Calories: 285
Protein: 34.4g
Carbohydrate: 23.8g
Fat: 5.8g

SERVES 4
WLS portion: ½

1 tsp each of ground ginger, ground coriander
   and turmeric
500g diced lean lamb
Fry Light low-fat cooking spray
1 onion, chopped
3 cloves garlic, crushed
2 large carrots, peeled and chopped
400g can chopped tomatoes
100g soft dried apricots, halved
300ml vegetable stock
2 tbsp soy sauce
salt and freshly ground black pepper

VARIATIONS

Chicken tagine: replace the lamb with 500g skinless and boneless chicken thighs. Cook for about 1½ hours until tender.

Vegetable tagine: replace the lamb with about 700g chopped vegetables such as butternut squash, potatoes, courgettes and peppers. Reduce the cooking time to 1 hour.

1. Preheat the oven to 150°C/gas mark 2.

2. Mix the ginger with the coriander and turmeric in a dish. Add the lamb and toss to mix. Leave to marinate for at least 30 minutes.

3. Spray a large non-stick pan with Fry Light. Add the lamb, in batches, and fry over a high heat until browned. Transfer to a tagine or casserole dish.

4. Lower the heat, add the onion and cook gently for 5 minutes. Add the garlic and carrots and cook for 2 minutes.

5. Add the tomatoes, apricots, stock, soy sauce and salt and pepper to taste. Bring to the boil, pour over the lamb, cover and cook for about 2 hours until tender. Serve with couscous if liked.

It's in the bag

Looking for a complete, low-fat meal that virtually cooks itself? Then be imaginative with baking parchment paper or foil parcels. There's no need for special cooking dishes, little need for lashings of oil but plenty of room for seasonings and flavourings to perk up the plainest of fish, chicken or meat fillets. Serve in the wrappings if liked, allowing the diners to open their parcels at the table for a heady aroma. When cutting out the paper or foil make sure it is big enough to completely enclose the chosen main ingredient.

Moroccan spiced chicken papilotes

Preheat the oven to 200°C/gas mark 6. Spray 4 foil squares with Fry Light low-fat cooking spray. Divide 1 sliced red onion, 410g can drained chickpeas, 2 sliced tomatoes, half a sliced Romano red pepper and 1 tbsp harissa paste between the foil sheets and season to taste. Divide 400g mini breast chicken fillets between the parcels, dot with a further 1 tbsp harissa paste and sprinkle evenly with 1 tsp saffron threads. Top with a few slices of preserved lemon and fold to secure. Bake for 25 minutes until cooked.

SERVES 4
WLS portion: ½

Calories: 260
Protein: 41.2g
Carbohydrate: 14.1g
Fat: 4.3g

Cod parcels with toasted seeds and vine tomatoes

Preheat the oven to 190°C/gas mark 5. Spray 4 parchment or foil squares with Fry Light olive oil spray. Top each with a 150g frozen wild Alaska Pacific cod fillet. Spread each with 1 tsp green pesto sauce and sprinkle with a little lemon juice. Toast 75g seed and nut mixture in a dry frying pan for 2-3 minutes, stirring constantly. Share between the parcels, add a small bunch of cherry vine tomatoes and spray again with Fry Light. Fold to secure and bake for 25-30 minutes until cooked.

SERVES 4
WLS portion: ½

Calories: 245
Protein: 30.5g
Carbohydrate: 9.5g
Fat: 9.1g

Salmon with sun-dried tomato, Parmesan and basil topping

Preheat the oven to 190°C/gas mark 5. Spray 4 foil squares with Fry Light. Top each with a 150g frozen wild Alaska salmon fillet. Mix 50g chopped sun-dried tomatoes with 4 tbsp grated Parmesan, 175g extra-light soft cheese and 1 tbsp chopped basil. Spread over the salmon and fold the foil to secure. Bake for 20-25 minutes, opening for the last 5 minutes.

SERVES 4
WLS portion: ½

Calories: 425
Protein: 43.2g
Carbohydrate: 3.4g
Fat: 26.5g

Roasted stuffed peppers with Parma ham

Thinly sliced Parma ham can be used to make such delicious meals – here it tops tasty peppers that are stuffed with couscous, spring onions, cherry tomatoes and parsley. You can use other vegetables instead of peppers – try large mushrooms, hollowed-out beef tomatoes or courgettes instead. For extra flavour and protein you could also add 75g crumbled feta cheese to the couscous stuffing mixture.

Calories: 260
Protein: 13g
Carbohydrate: 34.1g
Fat: 7.9g

SERVES 4
WLS portion: ½

150g couscous
1 tsp vegetable or chicken stock powder
4 spring onions, finely chopped
4 yellow or red sweet long peppers, halved lengthways and deseeded
6 cherry tomatoes, quartered
2 tbsp chopped parsley
4 tsp olive oil
8 slices Parma ham

1. Preheat the oven to 190°C/gas mark 5.
2. Put the couscous into a heatproof bowl with the stock powder and spring onions. Add boiling water to just cover the grains, then leave to soak and swell for 10 minutes.
3. Arrange the pepper halves, cut sides up, in a baking dish or roasting tin.
4. Fluff up the couscous grains with a fork and stir in the tomatoes and parsley. Spoon the mixture into the peppers and drizzle with the olive oil. Bake in the oven for 20-25 minutes, or until tender.
5. Serve, topped with the slices of Parma ham.

Pacific cod with lime, herb and Parmesan crust

This delicious herb and cheese crust can be used on pollock, haddock or salmon fillets, the topping works well on them all.

Calories: 205
Protein: 27.8g
Carbohydrate: 10.4g
Fat: 6.1g

SERVES 4
WLS portion: ½

Fry Light olive oil spray
4 Pacific cod fillets, about 125g each
finely grated zest and juice of 1 lime
50g fresh white or wholemeal breadcrumbs
1 tbsp chopped fresh dill, oregano or parsley
50g grated Parmesan cheese
salt and freshly ground black pepper
4 thin slices of lime

1. Preheat the oven to 200°C/gas mark 6.
2. Lightly spray a baking tray with the Fry Light and arrange the cod fillets on top. Sprinkle with the lime juice.
3. Mix the lime zest with the breadcrumbs, chosen herbs, three-quarters of the Parmesan and salt and pepper to taste.
4. Divide between the fish fillets, spreading over the surface of each one. Spray well with Fry Light and dust with the remaining Parmesan. Finally top each with a slice of lime.
5. Bake for 12-15 minutes, or until the fish is opaque and flakes easily when tested with a fork. Serve with fresh vegetables in season.

Wild Alaska salmon on Thai potatoes

This splendid salmon dish literally sings with the fresh flavours of Thai seasonings. If, however, you aren't keen on coriander replace with flat-leaf parsley.

 Purée

Calories: 435
Protein: 29g
Carbohydrate: 32.7g
Fat: 20.5g

SERVES 4
WLS portion: ⅓ - ½

400ml can reduced-fat coconut milk
300ml fish or vegetable stock
4 tsp red Thai curry paste
1½ tsp ginger paste
¾ tsp ground turmeric
¾ tsp chopped red chilli
1 bunch spring onions, chopped
675g new potatoes, scrubbed and cut into chunks
salt and freshly ground black pepper
4 wild Alaska salmon fillets, skinned
chopped fresh coriander to garnish (optional)

1. Put the coconut milk, stock, curry paste, ginger paste, turmeric, chilli and spring onions in a large, shallow pan or wok. Bring to the boil, reduce the heat and add the potatoes with salt and pepper to taste. Simmer the potatoes gently, without covering, for about 20 minutes or until almost tender, stirring occasionally.
2. Carefully place the salmon fillets on top of the potatoes and spoon some of the liquid over the top. Cover and simmer for 6-8 minutes, or until the fish is cooked.
3. Serve in shallow bowls, topped with some fresh coriander if liked.

Orechietti with Tenderstem broccoli and prawns

This delicious twist on a simple pasta dish can be on the table in just over 10 minutes! You can, of course, use any pasta shape and if half-fat crème fraîche is unavailable use low-fat soft or cream cheese (with or without herbs) instead.

 Purée

Calories: 292
Protein: 27g
Carbohydrate: 35.1g
Fat: 4.9g

SERVES 4
WLS portion: ½

400g dried orechietti pasta
200g Tenderstem broccoli
Fry Light olive oil spray
400g raw peeled prawns
3 cloves garlic, crushed
pinch of dried chilli flakes (optional)
50g half-fat crème fraîche
2 tbsp chopped flat leaf parsley
salt and freshly ground black pepper

1. Cook the orechietti pasta in boiling salted water according to the pack instructions.
2. Meanwhile, prepare the broccoli by cutting the florets off and slicing the stem. Steam or boil for about 3 minutes until tender.
3. While the broccoli is cooking, spray a non-stick pan with Fry Light, add the prawns, garlic and chilli flakes, if used, and sauté until pink and just cooked through. Add the crème fraîche, parsley and salt and pepper to taste, mixing well over a very low heat.
4. Add the cooked and drained pasta and the drained broccoli. Toss well to mix and serve at once.

Salsa, sauces and spreads

A spoonful of a salsa, sauce or flavoursome spread can lift the ordinary dish into something celebratory. Try a side of tomato salsa with a plain piece of grilled chicken or to top eggs or cottage cheese; a dollop of hummous with vegetable crudités or to top a jacket-baked potato; a drizzle of low-sugar mint sauce with roast lamb or to dress a salad; or a scoop of dip with crunchy breadsticks or prawns all the better for dunking – for where else can you get so much flavour and versatility for so few Calories?

Hummous

Put a 400g drained can of chickpeas in a blender with 2 tbsp tahini paste, a peeled clove of garlic and the juice of 2 lemons. Purée until smooth. Season to taste with salt and freshly ground black pepper.

SERVES 4
WLS portion: ½

Calories: 115
Protein: 5.8g
Carbohydrate: 9.1g
Fat: 6.2g

Tomato and coriander salsa

Place 2 large tomatoes, 3 cloves garlic, 2 tbsp lime juice, half a chopped small onion, 2 tbsp chopped coriander, 1 tsp chopped chilli (optional) and half a tsp ground cumin in a food processor. Process in bursts for either a chunky or smooth texture as liked. Season to taste before serving.

SERVES 4
WLS portion: ½

Calories: 26
Protein: 1g
Carbohydrate: 4.4g
Fat: 0.4g

Bariatric mint sauce

Place 80g pack fresh mint in a food processor. Process until finely chopped (alternatively, chop by hand until fine). Add 1 tbsp Splenda granulated sweetener and 150ml white wine vinegar, mixing well. Leave to stand for at least 1 hour before serving to allow the flavours to develop. Store in an airtight jar in the refrigerator for up to 4 weeks.

MAKES 200ml (about 14 servings)
WLS portion: ½ - ¾

Calories: 5
Protein: 0.3g
Carbohydrate: 0.4g
Fat: 0g

Minty broad bean dip

Cook 200g broad beans in boiling water for about 4-5 minutes. Drain and rinse under cold water. Remove the skins if a little tough. Put the beans, 200g fat-free Greek yogurt, a small handful of mint leaves, 20g Parmesan and half a clove of garlic in a food processor and blend until you have a thick green purée. Season to taste and serve with vegetable crudités.

SERVES 4
WLS portion: ½

Calories: 78
Protein: 8.1g
Carbohydrate: 7g
Fat: 2.1g

Turkey bolognese

Pasta bolognese has become a staple in the family diet and is usually made with beef. This version is particularly WLS friendly because it uses high protein and low saturated fat turkey mince and is just as flavoursome. Serve with spaghetti and grated Parmesan cheese if liked.

 Purée

Calories: 256
Protein: 32.3g
Carbohydrate: 10.8g
Fat: 9.4g

SERVES 4
WLS portion: ½

Fry Light low-fat cooking spray
1 large onion, finely chopped
500g turkey mince
1 clove garlic, crushed
2 carrots, peeled and diced
400g can chopped tomatoes in juice
2 tbsp tomato purée
200ml water
½ tsp dried oregano
1 tbsp Worcestershire sauce (optional)
salt and freshly ground black pepper

1. Spray a large, non-stick pan with Fry Light. Add the onion and cook over a gentle heat for 2-3 minutes to soften.
2. Increase the heat, add the turkey mince and cook for 1-2 minutes, stirring and breaking up any lumps.
3. Add the garlic, carrots, tomatoes, tomato purée, water, oregano, Worcestershire sauce, if used, and salt and pepper to taste. Bring to the boil, reduce the heat, cover and simmer for 45-50 minutes, until cooked and tender.
4. Serve hot with freshly cooked spaghetti and lightly dusted with Parmesan cheese if liked.

Chicken with oat, sage and apricot stuffing

Chicken thighs are often considered more pouch friendly than chicken breasts. Here they are combined with a tasty stuffing made with oats, apricots and sage. This is sure to become a family favourite recipe so ring the changes occasionally by replacing the apricots in the stuffing with dates or diced apple and toasted pinenuts. WLS patients should ideally remove the skin before serving.

Calories: 375
Protein: 45g
Carbohydrate: 41g
Fat: 2.9g

SERVES 4
WLS portion: ½

Fry Light low-fat cooking spray
8 chicken thighs, scored
15g fresh sage leaves
150g soft dried apricots
1 large onion, finely chopped
75g rolled porridge oats
100g wholemeal breadcrumbs
salt and freshly ground black pepper
6 tbsp water

1. Preheat the oven to 200°C/gas mark 6.
2. Heat a large frying pan until hot. Add a few sprays of Fry Light and the chicken, skin-side down. Fry for about 4-5 minutes until the skin is golden.
3. Transfer to a roasting tin or dish. Top each thigh with a whole sage leaf. Reserve 8 whole apricots and set aside.
4. Chop the remaining sage and remaining apricots.
5. Add the onion to the pan juices and cook over a gentle heat until golden.
6. Add the oats, breadcrumbs, sage, apricots and salt and pepper to taste, mixing well. Cook for a further 2 minutes, stirring well.
7. Remove from the heat, add the water and mix to make a stuffing. Divide and mould into 4 large stuffing balls and add to the roasting tin or dish.
8. Roast for 25-30 minutes, placing the reserved apricots on top of the chicken thighs halfway through cooking. Serve with freshly cooked vegetables.

Cauliflower and chicken curry

This is a mild and beautifully tender chicken curry that can be made with 3 tbsp masala curry paste instead of all the separate spices mentioned in step 3 below.

 Purée

Calories: 340
Protein: 30.4g
Carbohydrate: 13.4g
Fat: 17.7g

VARIATION

Vegetarian curry: Omit the chicken and add a 400g can drained chick peas at the same time as the tomatoes in the recipe opposite.

SERVES 4
WLS portion: ½

Fry Light low-fat cooking spray
6 large skinless and boneless chicken thighs, cut into bite-sized chunks
1 onion, finely chopped
2 green chillies, finely chopped
2 tsp ginger paste
3 cloves garlic, crushed
½ tsp chilli powder
1 tsp turmeric
2 tsp garam masala
2 tsp Splenda granulated sweetener
400g can chopped tomatoes
400ml can reduced-fat coconut milk
1 cauliflower, broken into florets
salt and freshly ground black pepper
2 large handfuls of fresh spinach

1. Heat a large frying pan, spray with Fry Light, then brown the chicken on all sides, about 5 minutes. Remove with a slotted spoon and set aside.
2. Add the onion and cook for 3-5 minutes until softened.
3. Add the chillies, ginger and garlic and cook for 1 minute. Add the chilli powder, turmeric, garam masala and Splenda, mixing well and cook for 1 minute.
4. Add the tomatoes, coconut milk, chicken and cauliflower. Mix well and simmer for 10-15 minutes until the chicken and cauliflower are cooked through and tender.
5. Season to taste then stir in the spinach. Cook briefly until the spinach wilts. Serve with rice or flatbreads if liked.

Quorn pasta carbonara

This is a wonderfully indulgent dish, suitable for vegetarians, since it uses Quorn bacon style rashers and mince. If you find that you are somewhat intolerant of egg yolks then leave them out, the dish is just as good, if just a little less creamy in texture. Serve with a little extra grated Parmesan if liked.

Purée

Calories: 390
Protein: 21.5g
Carbohydrate: 49.7g
Fat: 11.3g

SERVES 4
WLS portion: ½

225g dried spaghetti
Fry Light low-fat cooking spray
1 small onion or shallot, finely chopped
150g pack Quorn bacon style rashers, chopped
150g pack Quorn mince
100ml low-fat crème fraîche
2 egg yolks
pinch of ground nutmeg
2 tbsp chopped parsley
2 tbsp grated Parmesan cheese
salt and freshly ground black pepper

1. Cook the spaghetti in boiling salted water until cooked al dente, following pack instructions.
2. Meanwhile, spray a non-stick pan with Fry Light, add the onion or shallot, Quorn bacon style rashers and Quorn mince, mixing well. Cook gently for about 5-10 minutes until the onion is softened.
3. Mix the crème fraîche in a bowl with the egg yolks, nutmeg, half the parsley, Parmesan cheese and salt and pepper to taste.
4. Drain the cooked spaghetti, reserving 2 large spoonfuls of the cooking water. Return the pasta to the pan, add the Quorn mixture and the reserved cooking water, mixing well.
5. Add the crème fraîche mixture and stir gently, over a very low heat, until the ingredients are well combined.
6. Serve at once, sprinkled with the remaining parsley.

A new take on takeaway

Takeaways can be a real banana-skin for the WLS patient. No back of pack to check for nutritional information nor any guarantee that the dish hasn't got high levels of sugar and fat. Yet, from time to time, we fancy something from the Chinese and 'fish n chip' repertoire. The dishes on this page show how easy it is to make a takeaway at home and in little more time than it takes to order then wait for the delivery.

Prawn buckwheat noodles with soy and ginger shallots

Marinate 12 small, peeled shallots in 3 tbsp soy sauce and 1 tbsp chopped ginger for 20 minutes, then drain, reserving the marinade. Cook a 200g pack buckwheat noodles according to the pack instructions. Heat a wok until hot, spray with Fry Light, add the shallots and fry for 3 minutes. Add 1 finely chopped red chilli, 2 finely chopped cloves of garlic and 250g shelled large prawns. Fry for 2 minutes. Add 250g shredded spring greens and fry for 2 minutes until just tender. Pour in the reserved marinade and noodles and toss well to mix. Serve at once.

SERVES 4
WLS portion: ½ - ¾

Calories: 245
Protein: 21.8g
Carbohydrate: 35.5g
Fat: 1.9g

New style fish and strips

Cut 300g Alaska pollock into neat strips and roll in 3 tbsp sesame seeds. Heat 1 tbsp stir-fry oil in a wok or large pan, add the pollock and fry gently for 3-4 minutes, until golden. Remove and keep warm. Wipe out the pan with kitchen paper, reheat, spray with Fry Light, add 300g stir-fry vegetables and cook for 3-4 minutes. Add 2 tbsp sweet chilli sauce, 2 tbsp soy sauce and 1 tbsp lemon juice. Fry for 1 minute. Fold in the pollock strips and serve at once.

SERVES 2
WLS portion: ½ - ¾

Calories: 390
Protein: 35g
Carbohydrate: 12.4g
Fat: 21g

Sticky turkey stir-fry

Mix 2 tbsp soy sauce with the rind and juice of 1 orange, 2 tbsp honey, 1 tbsp wholegrain mustard and 450g turkey breast cut into strips. Heat a wok until hot, spray with Fry Light and add 2 thinly sliced carrots and 175g broccoli florets. Fry for 3 minutes. Add the turkey (reserving the marinade). Add 2 tbsp water, 2 tsp each of chopped garlic and ginger, 4 sliced spring onions and 2 sliced red peppers. Fry for 4 minutes. Mix 1 tbsp cornflour with the marinade, add and cook for 1-2 minutes. Serve at once.

SERVES 4
WLS portion: ½ - ¾

Calories: 256
Protein: 28.9g
Carbohydrate: 26.7g
Fat: 2.1g

Chicken and egg fried rice

Heat 1 tbsp oil in a wok. Add 1 chopped clove of garlic, 2 tsp grated ginger and 250g diced cooked chicken. Fry for 2 minutes. Add 300g stir-fry vegetables and 350g cooked rice. Fry for 2 minutes then transfer to a warm bowl. Add a further 1 tbsp oil to the wok, add 6 beaten eggs and cook for 1 minute to scramble. Add the chicken mixture with 4 tbsp soy sauce and toss to mix. Serve at once.

SERVES 4
WLS portion: ½

Calories: 390
Protein: 29.8g
Carbohydrate: 26.9g
Fat: 17.8g

Vanilla egg custards

I first made these custards about 1 week after surgery and they have featured on our weekly menu ever since. They are very gently set egg custards so I found they could be eaten in the full FLUIDS stage post-op. Later on I added a fruit base of chopped cherries, apricots and pears for variety.

Calories: 135
Protein: 9.3g
Carbohydrate: 9.8g
Fat: 6.4g

SERVES 7
WLS portion: ½ - 1

4 large eggs
410g can light evaporated milk
5 tbsp Splenda granulated sweetener
2 tsp vanilla extract
150ml skimmed milk
ground nutmeg to sprinkle (optional)

1. Preheat the oven to 170°C/gas mark 3.
2. Beat the eggs with the evaporated milk, Splenda, vanilla extract and skimmed milk. Sieve and pour into about 7 ramekin or heatproof cups.
3. Put inside a heatproof baking dish and add hand-hot water to come halfway up the sides of the ramekins or cups. Sprinkle the tops with a little ground nutmeg if liked.
4. Bake in the oven for 20-25 minutes until just set but still a bit wobbly.
5. Remove from the baking dish and allow to cool. Refrigerate to chill before serving.

Smooth chocolate dream

WLS doesn't mean the end of chocolate for life but it does mean that you have to be mindful of how to eat it. This recipe with a mixture of dry unsweetened chocolate and just a little dark plain chocolate gives the perfect balance, keeping the Calories and the fat low in a decadently-tasting dessert.

Calories: 102
Protein: 3.9g
Carbohydrate: 18.4g
Fat: 1.6g

SERVES 8
WLS portion: ½ - 1

35g Splenda granulated sweetener
2 tbsp unsweetened cocoa powder
50g cornflour
1 litre skimmed milk
35g dark plain chocolate, chopped
2 tsp vanilla extract
raspberries, mint sprigs and chopped nuts to decorate (optional)

1. Mix the Splenda in a small bowl with the cocoa powder. Mix the cornflour with about 200ml of the milk in another bowl until smooth.

2. Heat the remaining milk in a pan until just at scalding point. Whisk in the cocoa mixture, blending well. Remove from the heat and whisk in the cornflour mixture, beating constantly. Return to the heat and cook, stirring constantly, for about 10 minutes, or until the mixture is slightly thickened, smooth and glossy.

3. Remove from the heat, add the chocolate and vanilla and stir well to blend.

4. Pour the mixture into a large or 8 small serving dishes and cover with cling film (to prevent a skin from forming). Cool then chill for at least 2 hours before serving.

5. Serve decorated with raspberries, mint sprigs and chopped nuts if liked.

Herby fruit salad

Here is a twist on a classic fruit salad. The Asian influence of coriander and coconut milk make this an unusual but refreshing change to the run-of-the-mill offerings. Try it, you won't be disappointed!

Calories: 122
Protein: 1.3g
Carbohydrate: 27.1g
Fat: 1.3g

SERVES 6
WLS portion: ½ - ¾

4 tbsp reduced-fat coconut milk
1 tbsp clear honey
lemon or lime juice, to taste
2 blood oranges or 1 small pink grapefruit, peeled and sliced
1 small pineapple, peeled and chopped
1 pink-skinned apple, cored and chopped
1 banana, peeled and sliced
1 small mango, peeled, stoned and chopped
2 tbsp chopped fresh coriander

1. Mix the coconut milk with the honey and lemon or lime juice to taste.
2. Mix the oranges or grapefruit with the pineapple, apple, banana, mango and coriander.
3. Add the coconut milk dressing and toss well to mix. Serve lightly chilled.

Protein ice cream

In a quest to find a wonderful tasting protein drink I have sampled many an awful one! Some are just too sweet for my new palate. However, knowing that freezing diminishes sweetness and flavour they have come into their own as the basis for some superb protein ice creams. Rarely does a day pass when I don't have a scoop or two to boost my protein intake, or at least this is now my legitimate excuse! An ice cream maker will make light work of this recipe and its variations but isn't essential. Try it once and be prepared to become hooked!

Calories: 133
Protein: 27.2g
Carbohydrate: 6.3g
Fat: 0.1g

SERVES 4
WLS portion: ½ - 1

500ml skimmed milk
4 x 27g scoops vanilla whey protein isolate powder

1. Mix the milk with the protein powder in a large jug, beating well to mix.
2. Pour into an ice cream maker and process until softly whipped and frozen. Spoon into a large or 4 small freezer containers and freeze until firm. You could serve softly frozen at this stage. Alternatively, pour into a large freezer container and freeze until firm, whisking once or twice during the process to break down any large ice crystals.
3. Remove from the freezer about 30-60 minutes before serving to soften slightly for scooping. Serve with a little half-fat whipped cream, fruit and wafers if liked.

VARIATIONS

Chocolate protein ice cream: use 4 scoops chocolate whey protein isolate powder (I use Syntrax Nectar Chocolate Truffle) and 2 tbsp unsweetened cocoa powder.

Pina colada protein ice cream: use 4 scoops coconut/pineapple whey protein isolate powder (I use Syntrax Nectar Caribbean Cooler). Add 100g finely chopped fresh pineapple for last minute of churning in ice cream maker or fold in after last whisking by hand.

Frappuccino protein ice cream: use 2 scoops chocolate and 2 scoops coffee whey protein isolate powder (I use 4 scoops Syntrax Nectar Cappuccino).

Frozen assets

Traditional ready-made ice creams, water ices and frozen yogurts are generally off the menu for WLS patients – most simply have too much sugar or fat in them. However, making them at home from scratch is easy and means they can reappear without the risk of sugar or fat overload. An ice cream maker is a worthwhile investment if, like me, you love these ices at all times of year (and they do give a superior smoother finished texture). Otherwise, just remember to whisk once or twice during the freezing process to break down big ice crystals.

Frozen vanilla yogurt with raspberries

Toast 50g porridge oats in a frying pan until golden then cool. Mix 5 x 200g cartons Muller Light vanilla yogurt with a 150g tub low-fat custard and the oats. Freeze for 2 hours. Meanwhile, cook 250g crushed raspberries with 2 tbsp Splenda granulated sweetener over a low heat until softened, about 5 minutes. Stir into the yogurt mixture and freeze for 2-3 hours or in an ice cream maker. Remove from freezer 30 minutes before serving to soften slightly. Scoop to serve with extra raspberries and mint sprigs if liked.

SERVES 6
WLS portion: ½ - ¾

Calories: 145
Protein: 9.4g
Carbohydrate: 22.6g
Fat: 1.2g

Summer fruits ice

Place 125ml water, the pared rind and juice of 1 lemon and 1 orange and 20g Splenda granulated sweetener in a small pan. Bring to the boil, reduce the heat and simmer for 5 minutes. Allow to cool then strain. Place 320g pack defrosted frozen British summer fruits in a blender with the cool juice and purée until smooth. Freeze until firm or in an ice cream maker. Remove from freezer 30 minutes before serving to soften slightly. Scoop to serve with fresh strawberries if liked.

SERVES 6
WLS portion: ½ - ¾

Calories: 48
Protein: 0.9g
Carbohydrate: 11g
Fat: 0.2g

Mango crush

Place 125ml water, the pared rind and juice of 1 lemon and 1 orange and 12g Splenda granulated sweetener in a small pan. Bring to the boil, reduce the heat and simmer for 5 minutes. Allow to cool then strain. Place 350g mango pieces in a blender with the cool juice and purée until smooth. Freeze until firm or in an ice cream maker. Remove from the freezer 30 minutes before serving to soften slightly. Scoop to serve with extra mango slices and mint sprigs if liked.

SERVES 6
WLS portion: ½ - ¾

Calories: 88
Protein: 1.1g
Carbohydrate: 21.4g
Fat: 0.3g

Ratafia stuffed peaches

Nothing sings out summer more than white-fleshed peaches. This easy and deliciously quick to make recipe makes the most of them with a filling of creamy quark mixed with crushed ratafia biscuits. When not in season replace with canned peaches in natural juice.

Purée without skin

Calories: 95
Protein: 7.4g
Carbohydrate: 15g
Fat: 0.8g

SERVES 4
WLS portion: ½

4 fresh white-fleshed peaches, skinned if liked
20g or about 10 small ratafia biscuits
200g quark
2 tbsp Splenda granulated sweetener
2 tsp low-sugar squash or liqueur
mint leaves to garnish (optional)

1. Halve the peaches and remove and discard the stones.
2. Crush the ratafia biscuits and place in a bowl with the quark, Splenda and squash or liqueur. Mix well to combine.
3. Carefully spoon into the centre of each peach half.
4. Serve garnished with mint leaves if liked.

Oaty baked raspberry cheesecake

This cheesecake looks and tastes divine, but only takes moments to prepare. It is topped with fresh and fruity raspberries but could be decorated and served with almost any soft fresh fruit. I sometimes like to heat berries with about 3 tbsp low-sugar jam and a dash of water to make a soft fruit topping or purée the same to make an accompanying coulis. You could also add 50g sultanas to the cream cheese mixture.

Calories: 228
Protein: 12.3g
Carbohydrate: 20.6g
Fat: 10.8g

SERVES 8
WLS portion: ½

50g butter
50g clear honey
150g rolled porridge oats
400g low-fat cream cheese
3 medium eggs, separated
6 tbsp Splenda granulated sweetener
1 tsp vanilla extract
150g fresh raspberries

1. Preheat the oven to 180°C/gas mark 4.

2. Melt the butter and the honey in a saucepan then stir in the oats, mixing well. Press onto the base of a 20 cm round, loose-bottomed cake tin.

3. Whisk the cream cheese with the egg yolks, Splenda and vanilla extract until smooth.

4. Whisk the egg whites until stiff then fold into the cream cheese mixture. Pour into the cake tin.

5. Bake in the oven for 35-40 minutes or until golden and just firm to the touch. Allow to cool before removing from the tin and transferring to a serving plate.

6. Chill well then top with raspberries to serve.

Acknowledgements and links

As with all books, there are more people involved in the conception and production of the publication than the author's name on the jacket. I am personally indebted to my colleagues, Amy, Kate and Anna at **Eight & Four** (www.eightandfour.com) whose belief and enthusiasm for this project, in the very early days, led to their development and launch of my website www.bariatriccookery.com. Their support beyond the normal confines of interested web designers has been amazing.

My book designers **Rumseyshort** made the job of self-publication a most pleasurable one. Rob Short welcomed my initial approach and Andrea Rumsey took control and held my hand throughout. The book you see is as much hers as mine, I couldn't have done it without her and she was a joy and inspiration to work with. I hope we can work on a sequel.

Many good and loyal old friends, and new ones that I have made on Forums, at Support Groups and within the weight-loss surgery community must be thanked. They told me what they wanted from a book and what food topics they needed help with. Due to confidentiality I can't name them but they all know who they are and I salute you!

Countless public relation agencies helped with sourcing images and information for recipes and for the introductory pages (they are listed opposite) – their help proved invaluable.

The gym and spa team at **Nirvana Spa** (www.nirvanaspa.co.uk) must also be applauded and commended for their resolve in getting me moving and providing advice for others who have had bariatric (weight-loss) surgery. You will be seeing more of me, although I hope to be sitting on the loser's bench!

My own surgeon, **Shaw Somers**, and his team at **Streamline Surgical** made the whole thing possible and gave me, not only a new 'oppiversary date' to celebrate each year, but a new life too. Stacey Brova, Patient Care Co-ordinator for Streamline Surgical; Louise Hall, my Bariatric Nurse at the Hampshire Clinic; Shayna Griffiths, Specialist Bariatric Dietician; Toni Russo, Streamline's Bariatric Nurse Consultant; David Steene, CEO of Streamline Surgical LLP; Shelley Frosdick, Public Relations Manager at PHA (and also my Editor on 'Thinner Times'); and Kathy Ling, my link to them all – I give you my heart-felt thanks.

Last but not least I must thank my family – husband Peter who took many of the beautiful photographs for the book and website; my daughter Lucinda for her work on press releases and publicity; and my son Charlie for being an enthusiastic if sometimes unknowingly recipe sampler – they all put up with a lot when the book was 'cooking'.

Recipe and image credits

All about oats
www.allaboutoats.com (pages 82, 97, 102)

Bariatric Cookery (UK) Ltd
www.bariatriccookery.com (pages 1, 15, 23, 24, 25, 28, 32, 34, 35, 36, 40, 46, 58, 63, 67, 77, 90, 92, 98, 100, 105, 112)

British Lion Eggs
www.britegg.co.uk (pages 38, 42, 50, 88)

British Peas and Beans
www.tastesofsummer.co.uk (pages 52, 78, 112)

English Provender
www.englishprovender.com (pages 29, 44, 112)

Fish 4 Ever
www.fish-4-ever.com (page 48)

Flour Advisory Bureau
www.fabflour.co.uk (page 62)

Gut week; Recipe by Anthony Worrall-Thompson on behalf of Gut Week;
www.loveyourgut.com (page 94)

I Love British Turkey;
www.ilovebritishturkey.co.uk (pages 56, 80, 88)

Kikkoman
www.kikkoman.co.uk (page 66)

Love your Greens
www.loveyourgreens.co.uk (page 84)

Parma Ham Consortium
www.prosciuttodiparma.com (page 70)

Quorn
www.quorn.co.uk (pages 49, 56, 86)

Schwartz
www.schwartz.co.uk (page 64)

Tenderstem Broccoli
www.tenderstem.co.uk (page 76)

The Alaska Seafood Marketing Institute, Photography by Steve Lee; Recipe and Food Styling by Sue Ashworth
www.alaskaseafood.org (pages 42, 49, 55, 61, 68, 72, 74, 87)

Two Chicks
www.twochicks.co.uk (pages 16, 55)

UK shallots
www.ukshallots.com (pages 62, 87)

Waitrose, where more than 5,000 recipes can be viewed at
www.waitrose.com (pages 36, 41, 54)

Information credits

Bariatric Advantage
www.bariatricadvantage.com

Gravitas
www.gravitas-ltd.co.uk

Streamline Surgical
www.streamline-surgical.com

The Hospital Group
www.thehospitalgroup.org

Stockist

Of Syntrax Nectar Whey Protein Isolate Powder
www.predatornutrition.com

Links

American Society for Metabolic and Bariatric Surgery (ASMBS)
www.asbs.org

British Obesity and Metabolic Surgery Society
www.british-obesity-surgery.org

National Institute for Health and Clinical Excellence (NICE)
www.nice.org.uk

National Obesity Forum
www.nationalobesityforum.org.uk

Obesity Surgery Website
www.obesitysurgery.org.uk

The British Obesity Surgery Patient Association (BOSPA)
www.bospa.org

bariatriccookery.com

If you are thinking about, have had or are scheduled for bariatric (weight-loss) surgery – Gastric Bypass, Lap Band, Gastric Sleeve or Duodenal Switch, then this is the UK's number one website to support your new eating regime.

Carol Bowen Ball, a gastric bypass patient, and her team, have the food information, recipes and ideas to nourish, feed and inspire you.

It's essential that bariatric patients follow strict guidelines concerning protein, fat, sugar and overall Calories for weight-loss success. Patients also need to adhere to the 3 stages of eating from Fluids (straight after surgery); via Soft Foods, to finally Eating for Life. You'll find advice on what to eat through these stages, the recipes to use and menus and ideas for all occasions.

The blog, updated regularly, will have seasonal recipes; foodie news (be they product or equipment related); events of interest; the latest findings and research on obesity and weight-loss surgery; fashion and beauty tips for the 'shrinking losers'; discussions on coping mechanisms and strategies for before and after surgery; and anything else food, fat or fabulously-related!

Oh and some real-life stories... for inspiration!

www.bariatriccookery.com